D0272608

A PINCH OF
HERBS

A PINCH OF
HERBS

Herbs for Beauty, Health & Cookery
Recipes & Traditions

KATY HOLDER & GAIL DUFF

PUBLISHED BY THE READER'S DIGEST ASSOCIATION LIMITED
LONDON • SYDNEY

A READER'S DIGEST BOOK

Published by The Reader's Digest Association Limited
Berkeley Square House
Berkeley Square
London W1X 6AB

Copyright © 1997 Quarto Publishing plc
All rights reserved. No part of this publication may be reproduced,
stored in a retrieval system or transmitted in any form or by any means,
electronic, mechanical, photocopying, recording or otherwise, without
the permission of the copyright holder.

ISBN 0 276 42284 8

This book was designed and produced by
Quarto Publishing plc
The Old Brewery
6 Blundell Street
London N7 9BH

Senior Art Editor: Clare Baggaley
Assistant Art Editor: Sally Bond
Editor: Cathy Marriott
Copy Editors: Mary Senechal, Deborah Savage
Designer: Allan Mole
Picture Researcher: Susannah Jayes
Picture Research Manager: Giulia Hetherington
Photographer: David Sherwin
Photographer's Assistant: Lee Patterson
Stylist: Maureen Kane
Illustrators: Jane Smith, Elisabeth Dowle
Art Director: Moira Clinch
Assistant Art Director: Penny Cobb
Editorial Director: Mark Dartford

Typeset in Great Britain by Central Southern Typesetters, Eastbourne
Manufactured in Hong Kong by Regent Publishing Services Ltd
Printed in China by Leefung-Asco Printers Ltd

® Readers Digest. The Digest and the Pegasus logo are registered
trademarks of the Reader's Digest Association, Inc., of Pleasantville,
New York, USA

CONTENTS

6   *Introduction*

8   *Herb–growing Through the Ages*

10   *Herb Lore*

12   *Growing Herbs*

16   *Preserving Herbs*

18   *Medical Herbalism*

20   *Herbal Treatments in the Home*

22   *Aromatic Herbs*

26   *Herb Directory*

28   *Herbal Beauty*

32   *Culinary Herbs*

34   *Herbs in the Kitchen*

38   *Starters and Snacks*

56   *Vegetables and Salads*

74   *Meat and Poultry*

92   *Fish and Shellfish*

110   *Sauces, Relishes and Dips*

126   *Index*

128   *Acknowledgements*

INTRODUCTION

"What is a herb?" asked Alcuin, Abbot of the monastery of St Martin at Tours in France. And the Emperor Charlemagne, who had asked him to draw up a list of plants for the Imperial gardens, replied: "A herb is the friend of physicians and the praise of cooks."

Charlemagne, the emperor of France and the Holy Roman Empire in the 8th and 9th centuries, commissioned a list of plants and herbs grown in the Imperial Gardens.

A herb is a plant whose leaves, flowers and, sometimes, stems are put to a purpose that enhances our lives. Herbs are valued in the kitchen where they give a special flavour to sweet and savoury dishes; they can be used in preparations to scent our bodies and our surroundings; and they can be used as natural medicines. Most herbs contain an aromatic oil, often called the essential oil, which gives them their characteristic scent, flavour and healing properties. Another distinguishing feature is, whatever the use to which herbs are put, usually only small amounts are needed to attain the desired effect.

In years gone by, the term herb was applied to any green plant, including cabbages, celery and artichokes. Today, however, we confine the name to the small, powerful plants that add zest to our lives and delight to our surroundings. They have always been loved and, although they were largely neglected in the early years of the 20th century, their properties are now even more highly valued.

In an age of tinned foods, artificial flavourings, chemical cures, and even fresh-air sprays in a can, there came a backlash. We looked back to an era when life moved at a slower pace, an era of aromatic gardens, of still-rooms, of pot-herbs, of the remedies of the wise woman – and we rediscovered herbs.

The world was getting smaller as people travelled to foreign countries and brought back fresh ideas and ethnic communities with their own cooking styles settled in this country. In order to reproduce newly discovered dishes, we needed the herbs to make them taste authentic. Supermarkets and markets observed the trend, and now a wide range of herbs, both

A field of fragrant lavender waiting to be harvested, at Norfolk Lavender Ltd, Hediam, Norfolk, England.

Dried herbs – including fennel, chervil, tarragon, parsley and chives – for sale in Vaison-la-Romaine Market, Vaucluse, France.

almost intangible. In a world full of mechanical gadgets and of entertainment at the push of a button, we need an experience that we can achieve for ourselves and, in doing so, acquire a certain amount of satisfaction. Herbs can provide this. Whether you are flavouring a special dish, making a gargle to ease a sore throat, perfuming a room or beautifying yourself with a face pack, you are creating something that will improve your life – and that is important to us all.

If you go one step further and grow your own herbs, then you will really be able to appreciate them. In preparing the ground (or the flower pot), sowing the seed, nurturing and planting out the seedlings, and watching them grow, you will be taking part in the natural cycle of the seasons. You can enjoy the experience, take pride in your achievement, and benefit from the results. Herbs are not just the province of physicians and cooks – they are the friend and the praise of everyone.

Fragrant herbs flourish in a south-facing walled garden. This garden contains a range of herbs, including eau de cologne mint, lavender, comfrey, sage, rosemary and scented geraniums.

fresh and dried, is available to everybody. Besides using them in new-found dishes, we can explore the older recipe books and reproduce the forgotten flavours of our own past.

To maintain their health, people have also turned to herbs for gentle cures with no side-effects and to holistic practitioners who treat the whole person rather than one symptom. Herbs have featured prominently in this search. Herbal medicine and its associated treatments, such as aromatherapy, have become a respected form of healthcare; ideas from all over the world are being collected together for study, and more scientific research is being conducted into the effectiveness of herbs than ever before. The aromatic properties of herbs have long been recognised. The mere presence in a room of a sweet herbal scent, however gentle, can lift the spirits and make being in that place more pleasant. We have also become more aware of the suffering that we can cause other living creatures in the name of beauty. Herbal cosmetics are kinder to animals and to our skins.

Culinary, medicinal, aromatic, cosmetic: these, then, are the properties of herbs. But there is something else – something that is

HERB-GROWING THROUGH THE AGES

When herbs were first used and man was nomadic, they had to be sought in the wild whenever they were needed. At the time of the first farmers, around 6000 BC, when people began to have permanent homes, herbs were transplanted to convenient plots near dwellings. This was the beginning of herb gardening.

The first Roman emperor, Augustus, crowned with laurel. Laurel wreaths were a Roman symbol of victory and were also worn by conquering soldiers and athletes.

A knight, page and squire from late medieval times when most households grew herbs.

We know that the ancient Egyptians valued herbs for medicinal, culinary and aromatic purposes. They were excellent gardeners, and plans survive of the elaborate gardens that they laid out on the banks of the Nile. Herbs and other plants were arranged in straight rows, with paths in between them. There were water channels for irrigation, and a wall or fence around the whole plot.

Herbs are frequently mentioned in the Bible, and throughout the Middle East, herb gardens were usually attached to temples and to sacred groves. Details survive, inscribed on stone tablets, of the herb gardens of King Ashurbanipal of Assyria in 668 BC. In pre-Christian Europe, herbs were also connected with religion and were grown to be used in ceremonies by the Druids and others, as well as for general every-day purposes.

The Romans used quantities of herbs; lavender and rosemary were their favourites. They learned about herb gardening from the Egyptians, and soon after their capture of Egypt began to include a *hortus* in their villa gardens. The hortus was an area for growing herbs and vegetables, usually in separated beds or rows. Herbs were also grown in terra-cotta pots, which were placed along walkways and around courtyards. The Romans took herbs to every country that they conquered, so the rosemary and thyme of the hot Mediterranean regions were soon to be found growing in Britain and northern Europe.

After the fall of the Roman Empire, many herbs were lost through lack of interest in their cultivation. Others escaped from the one-time villa gardens and became naturalised in their new countries. Herbs were still used, but not on such a grand scale. It was the monks who kept the art of herb gardening alive through the Dark Ages. In Anglo-Saxon times, the monastery herb gardens were quite small. A plan drawn up by the monks of St Gall in nineteenth century Switzerland records only 16 herbs, and the 9th-century German monk Walafrid Strabo had a similar list. At this time, gardens were for use and not for beauty. All plants were grown for a purpose – and most of them were herbs.

In the more settled medieval times, the range of garden herbs was extended, partly because the Crusaders brought home new ideas and plants from the East and from the Mediterranean. Every household grew a few plants, but it was still the monks who excelled at herb gardening, and they who were called upon to tend the sick in all communities.

As early as the 14th century, however, there emerged commercial herb growers, who cultivated their plants on plots close to town centres and sold bunches of herbs from stalls or cried them in the streets. After the Black Death that devastated Europe in the 14th century, more land became available for those who had survived. Greater numbers of people became tenant farmers with enough land to set aside for wider ranges of herbs, as well as fruits and vegetables, for family use. From then on, it was the women who took charge of these plots, growing the herbs that were most suited to their family's needs.

In Tudor times, gardens gradually became larger and more people turned to gardening for pleasure. Culinary, medicinal and aromatic herbs were important in every household, and

An aerial view of the grounds of Chateau Villandoi, in the Loire region of France, showing the pattern of the formal knot garden.

But apart from the use to be made of herbs, how beautiful an old herb garden is, and how altogether lovable.

ELEANOR SINCLAIR RHODE, *A GARDEN OF HERBS,* 1920s

there were herb gardens attached to both town and country homes. Where there was no land, herbs were grown in pots.

During this period, gardens began to be designed, and the first knot gardens were devised, influenced by the patterns of oriental carpets which had become popular with the rich. The knots were intended to be viewed from above and were placed under the windows of the most important rooms of the house. The design was carpet-like, and every plant in it had a significance. The beds of herbs were outlined with low hedges or evergreen herbs, such as marjoram, hyssop or thyme and, later, box. Some were planted in intricate, lover's-knot patterns; some were simple rectangular beds.

To relieve the formality of the garden, somewhere nearby was a "wild" section, called a "wilderness garden", where herbs could grow almost at random and where their scent was released when they were trodden underfoot. Camomile lawns, which served the same purpose, became popular in Elizabethan times.

Many herbals and gardening books were written in the period between the late 16th and early 18th centuries. At the same time, large physic gardens were established for the cultivation of medicinal herbs. Some were privately owned by herbalists and apothecaries,

who grew herbs for their practices. The last such garden in London was in operation until 1828. Others, such as the Orto Botanico in Pisa and the Orto dei Semplici in Florence, were for the use of universities and other public bodies.

During the 18th century, herb gardens became less formal and, although some of the larger houses kept their knot gardens, herbs were increasingly grown in beds and borders to give the impression of random planting. This style has prevailed to the present day.

Although country people and those with big houses maintained their herb gardens throughout the 19th century, there was little room in cities for such luxuries. In many European countries, the first half of the 20th century saw a decline of interest in herbs, but a revival in the 1960s has since caused many people to begin growing them again. In the last 20 years, many new herb farms have been set up all over the world to supply individual growers with plants and seeds and the commercial world with natural ingredients for food and remedies.

Bergamot was discovered in North America in the 17th century by early settlers. It became popular in European herb gardens because of its dramatic red flowers, sweet aroma and use as a medical herb.

HERB LORE

MANY HERBS HAVE BEEN ENDOWED WITH MAGICAL PROPERTIES. THEY HAVE BEEN USED AS PROTECTIONS AND LOVE CHARMS; THEY HAVE BEEN ASSOCIATED WITH DIFFERENT GODS AND GODDESSES; AND THEY HAVE BEEN PART OF THE RITES OF BIRTH, MARRIAGE AND DEATH.

Some herbs have been considered sacred, a gift of the gods, such as angelica in Scandinavia and eastern Europe, and mint in France and Spain. Some of these "holy" plants were sacred to particular gods or godesses while others were simply special. The Anglo-Saxons had nine sacred herbs: fennel, mugwort, plantain, watercress, camomile, nettle, chervil, crab-apple and atterlothe, which has never been identified in modern terms.

Plantain, one of the nine sacred plants of the Anglo-Saxons.

SOWING, PLANTING AND HARVESTING

Herbs that are hard to grow or that take a long time to germinate generally have the most lore associated with their planting. Parsley is a notoriously slow grower, and the legend is widespread that it visits the devil nine (or sometimes seven) times before sprouting. In some parts of England, it was always planted on Good Friday to prevent the devil from getting involved and to ensure good luck and happiness for the coming year. In other places it was considered unlucky to sow the seeds across the garden, instead of along it. "It takes an honest man to grow parsley well" is one saying. "Parsley only grows where the missus is master" is another. And in the southern states of America it was thought unlucky to take parsley plants to the garden of a new house.

When it comes to harvesting herbs, the recommended times to do so were once governed by the phases of the moon. Some herbs could only be cut with certain implements. It was not thought right, for example, to cut mint with iron.

PROTECTIONS

People have hung bunches of herbs on doors, over beds and in other parts of the house to protect them against evil spirits and demons, nightmares, diseases and the supposed effects of witchcraft. Basil was hung in Hindu households to safeguard the spirit of the family. Rosemary was a popular protection in Spanish and Italian houses, and in Spain travellers wore it in their hats to ward off evil on the road. Rosemary placed under the pillow was thought to prevent nightmares. In Britain, vervain, dill and St John's wort were the herbs to deter witches, but they also featured in midsummer spells. Fennel was hung on doors, stuffed into keyholes and hung from the rafters on midsummer's eve to keep evil away.

HERBS OF THE GODS AND GODDESSES

The Greeks had many sacred plants. Bay (laurel) was dedicated to Apollo and to his son Asclepius, the god of medicine. The nymph Daphne was said to have been transformed into a bay tree to save her from the pursuit of Apollo. He made himself a bay wreath as a consolation. Menthe (mint) was another nymph, who was loved by Hades of the Underworld, and was turned into a mint plant by his wife Persephone out of jealousy.

The Holy Herbs Charm

Thyme and Fennel, two exceeding mighty ones,
These herbs the wise Lord made
Holy in the Heavens; He let them down,
Placed them, and sent them into the seven worlds
As a cure for all, the poor and the rich.

PASSED DOWN BY ORAL TRADITION. DATE AND AUTHOR UNKNOWN.

Rosemary

*A sprig of it hath a dumb language that meketh
it the chosen emblem of our funeral wakes and in our
buriall grounds.*

SIR THOMAS MORE, 16TH CENTURY

CHRISTIAN ASSOCIATIONS

There are many Christian legends surrounding rosemary. In Spain it was revered as one of the bushes that gave shelter to the holy family during the flight into Egypt. The flowers changed from white to blue when the Virgin Mary hung her cloak on a rosemary bush while she rested. Rosemary was said to grow to the same height as Christ, and after 33 years (his age when he died), the bush would become

Lovage, with its pungent, celery-scented leaves, was once worn in a small bag around the neck to attract a sweetheart.

wider but no higher. Wild thyme and fennel were other herbs associated with the Virgin Mary, and they were used together in charms.

HERBS AS SYMBOLS

The same herb sometimes represents different meanings in different places and times. In contrast to basil's high status in the Hindu world, the ancient Greeks associated it with poverty and misfortune, symbolised by a ragged woman with a pot of basil at her side. Fennel has been a symbol of flattery as well as honour; marigolds have variously stood for jealousy, constancy and obedience; sage has been an insult; camomile a sign of humility; and rosemary symbolised the fidelity of lovers. Fennel, thyme and borage endured as symbols of courage. Roman soldiers and gladiators ate fennel seeds to gain bravery; and Lancastrian ladies embroidered a bee hovering over wild thyme on the scarves they gave to their knights fighting the Wars of the Roses in the 15th century.

LOVE AND MARRIAGE

Many are the herbs that have been put into love charms and aphrodisiacs, and which have been carried or strewn at weddings to bring good luck and fertility. Basil has long been linked with love. In Crete it was called "love washed with tears"; and in Moldavia, it was said that a young man would fall in love with any girl from whom he accepted a sprig of basil. A favourite aphrodisiac was coriander, alone or mixed with violets and valerian. Lovage, savory, dill and tarragon have all been ingredients of love potions. Rosemary was a favourite wedding herb throughout Europe in the 16th and 17th centuries. Bridal posies have included dill for luck, marigolds for constancy, and rosemary for remembrance and fidelity.

IMMORTAL HERBS

In China it was thought that eating coriander would make you immortal, but people in other countries were content to believe that it simply prolonged life. In the French language of flowers, rosemary represents the rekindling of lost energy. Bankes's *Herbal*, published in England in 1525, says: "Make thee a box of the wood of Rosemary and smell to it and it shall preserve thy youth." The Laplanders looked to their sacred herb angelica to prolong life, chewing it and smoking it like tobacco.

11

GROWING HERBS

FOR A CONSTANT SUPPLY OF GOOD-QUALITY, FRESH HERBS, THERE IS NO BETTER WAY THAN GROWING THEM YOURSELF. MOST HERBS FLOURISH IN A LIGHT, WELL-DRAINED SOIL.

Herbs are simple to cultivate: they establish themselves easily, grow quickly and need little attention. Large amounts of space are not necessary: herbs will flourish in a small, sunny corner of the garden; in tubs and pots on the patio; in windowboxes or hanging baskets; and in small pots on the kitchen windowsill.

FINDING AND PREPARING AN OUTDOOR SITUATION

Before you choose your herbs, decide where your herb garden is going to be and how you

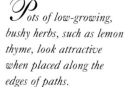

Pots of low-growing, bushy herbs, such as lemon thyme, look attractive when placed along the edges of paths.

Stunning displays can be achieved by placing pots of herbs within a design of herb beds and borders. Here, lemon balm forms the feature in this patio-style herb garden.

will design it. Decide which herbs you are going to grow and how you will arrange them.

It is probable that your range of herbs will have originated from more than one country and even from more than one type of habitat. You therefore have to find a soil and site that are a good compromise, in which the majority of the herbs will flourish.

Most herbs enjoy a light, dry, well-drained soil. The ideal site is within easy reach of the house, in a sheltered and sunny spot – preferably south-facing. A little shade on one side will help plants such as woodruff which do not like the full sun. Alternatively, you could create a shady patch nearby by arranging piles of brushwood around the area or by sticking twigs in the ground to make a "fence."

There are also herbs, such as valerian and bergamot, which prefer damp growing conditions. If you have space, create an artificially damp area by burying a perforated sheet of polythene 30–45 cm (12–18 in) under the surface and watering regularly.

Soil for herb-growing should be enriched with organic compost or well-rotted farmyard manure, or with a commercial organic product. Use a combination recommended for herb-growing by the manufacturers. If soil is on the acid side, a little lime can be added to it.

OTHER PLACES TO GROW HERBS

RAISED BEDS

If you have a small garden, a raised bed makes an ideal feature. Old bricks, local stone, even logs can be used to make the walls of the bed. Line the bottom with stones or rubble to allow for good drainage, and fill the bed with three parts topsoil to which you have added two parts peat and one and a half parts grit or gritty sand. Trailing plants are ideal to soften the edges of raised beds. Build up the height of the plants towards the back, if the bed is against a wall, or the centre, if the bed is free-standing.

ROCK GARDENS AND SLOPING GARDENS

You can build rock gardens and sloping gardens on naturally occurring slopes, or you can build them up artificially with a layer of rubble, one of gravel, and finally topsoil as above.

GRAVEL PATHS

Herbs originating from dry countries, for example, lavender, thyme and santolina, flourish on gravel paths. To keep the plants healthy, the path needs careful preparation. Dig it out to a depth of 30 cm (12 in) and

A herb garden should be essentially a garden enclosed; a sanctuary of sweet and placid pleasure; a garden of peace and of sweet scents.

ELEANOR SINCLAIR RHODE, *A GARDEN OF HERBS*, 1920s

half-fill it with rubble. Cover this with upturned slices of turf (cut from the ground), about 10 cm (4 in) thick and measuring approximately 30 x 45 cm (12 x 18 in) to provide moisture and soil. Finally, add a covering layer of gravel.

CHOOSING YOUR HERBS

A good way to choose the herbs that will best suit your needs and your plot is to obtain some catalogues from reputable herb farms. These usually contain all the information that you will need to know, such as main uses (culinary, aromatic or medicinal), how the herbs grow (annual, biennial or perennial), preferred growing situation and soil type, and height of the fully grown plants. They will also indicate whether you can buy seeds, plants or both.

A 17th-century herb garden, enclosed within railings and consisting of raised beds of varying shapes.

13

Herbs always look attractive against a background of gravel. These are actually grown in a brick-enclosed circle in the gravel path.

Growing Herbs in Tubs and Pots

Herbs can be grown in tubs, pots, window-boxes and half-barrels of countless shapes and sizes. To prepare the containers, cover the bottom with stones or pieces of broken terra-cotta pots. If the tubs are large, line them with upturned slices of turf. Cover these with a mixture of soil and shingle, and add ten parts fresh loam mixed with one part lime and bone meal, mixed. Tubs should be filled to within 5 cm (2 in) of the top.

To keep herbs indoors, choose pots to fit a sunny window-sill. Put a stone into the bottom of each pot and fill with a soil-based potting compost. Place the pots in small trays. Water the herbs from the bottom, letting them dry out completely between waterings. Feed them regularly during the growing season with any plant food suitable for potted plants.

Growing Herbs from Seed

If you want more than two of each plant, it is worth growing herbs from seed. For plants to be ready in the spring, sow your seeds indoors in the autumn. Have a different seed tray for each herb and fill it with a medium loam gritty compost, which gives good drainage and aeration. Sprinkle on the seeds, making sure that they are well spaced out, and cover them with a little more compost. Water the seeds very lightly, cover the tray with a sheet of glass or clear plastic and put it in a warm place,

out of direct sunlight, until the seeds begin to germinate. Keep the compost damp.

When the first seedlings appear, remove the cover and put the tray into brighter light. Water them regularly. When the seedlings are about 4 cm (1½ in) high, transfer them to small pots filled with fresh potting soil. In the spring, harden the plants off by putting them outside during the day and bringing them in at night. After two weeks, they should be ready for planting out.

Most annual and perennial seeds can be planted outdoors in the spring, and biennial seeds in the autumn. After the seeds have germinated, thin them out if necessary, or wait until they have grown more sturdy and transplant them.

Other Means of Propagation

Cuttings

This method is ideal for the shrubby herbs, such as rosemary, thyme, sage, hyssop and lavender. Cut a short piece of stem (about 7.5 cm (3 in) long) from the main plant, just below a leaf joint. Put the cutting into a potting medium in a small pot, water it lightly and cover it with a jam-jar for a week to keep it humid. Remove the jam-jar and allow the cutting to grow to about twice its size before planting out. (Each herb will take a different length of time.) Some cuttings, such as those

Even if you have only a small space you can still grow herbs successfully. A parsley pot can overflow with a wide selection of herbs.

from mint and rosemary, will root if they are simply put into a jar of water. Transfer them to a pot as soon as the roots develop.

ROOT CUTTINGS

With plants such as mint that spread by means of runners, take off a section of the horizontal root that has a stem coming from it. Put it into a potting medium and keep it humid for the first week. Keep the plant in the pot for a further four weeks, ensuring the potting medium stays moist, before planting out.

ROOT DIVISION

This is suitable for perennial plants over two years old. Dig them up and either pull the roots apart or cut them with a knife. When you are dealing with plants that have large, spreading roots, such as sorrel, cut the roots crossways into short lengths with a knife. Put them into the ground where you want them to grow.

These herbs have been grown in strips in the compartments of a polystyrene container and are now ready for either re-potting or planting out in the garden.

A wheel-shaped bed makes an attractive and easy-to-tend herb plot. This one has been newly planted.

PRESERVING HERBS

IF YOU GROW MORE FRESH HERBS THAN YOU CAN USE, THE ANSWER IS TO PRESERVE SOME OF THEM FOR THE WINTER.

The characteristic scents and flavours of herbs are produced by the essential oils of the plants. In order to maintain the aroma and the taste, these essential oils must be preserved by careful gathering.

HARVESTING

The greatest amount of oil is produced just before the plant flowers, so this is the best time to harvest herbs for preserving. Choose a dry, warm day, after the dew has dried but before the sun has become really hot. Cut the herbs with sharp scissors or secateurs and handle the sprigs carefully. You can safely cut away about one-third of perennial herbs, shaping the plants as you do so. Annual plants can be cut to a height of about 10 cm (4 in). Taking out their centre spike will encourage side shoots to grow. Cut only as many herbs as you can process in one day, and take them indoors, out of the sunlight, as soon as possible. Discard any damaged or diseased twigs or leaves.

DRYING HERBS

Herbs can be dried in bunches or on racks. They shrink as they dry, so tie bunches with strips of stretchy fabric (for example, from outworn pairs of thick tights) cut about 2.5 cm (1 in) wide, as they will fall out of string ties. Make a loop for hanging in one end of the strip, and cut a slit in the other end. Pass the strip once round approximately six herb sprigs. Put the looped end through the slit and pull the strip tight before hanging up. As the herbs dry,

During harvesting in Provence, lavender is often tied in bunches. Afterwards, the bunches are left to dry in a cool, airy place.

16

the tie will pull tighter to keep them secure.

Hang your bunches of herbs in a warm, dry, airy room or out-building, away from steam and excessive heat. The temperature should not exceed 30°C (90°F).

If you dry herbs frequently, you may like to construct your own drying racks. Make rectangular frames of light wood, strengthened with diagonal cross-pieces, and cover them with muslin. The racks can be placed side by side on a worktop or you can design them so that they stack. If you are adding herbs to the rack over a period of time, always put the freshest on the top rack, so that the moisture evaporates and rises from them freely, and is not absorbed by other plants.

In ideal conditions, herbs should be dry in four to five days. They should remain a bright, fresh colour, the twigs should snap easily and the leaves should be crisp.

Drying Herbs in a Microwave Oven

To dry herbs in a microwave oven, chop them finely and spread them out on a double layer of paper towels. Microwave them on high for 1½ minutes. The more delicate herbs may be quite dry by this time. Others should be stirred around and set to cook for a further minute. Check them once more, and stir and microwave again if necessary until the herbs are dry, crisp and bright green.

Storing Dried Herbs

Strip the leaves carefully from the stems and leave them whole. This will preserve more flavour than crumbling them.

Store dried herbs in airtight and lightproof containers, such as wood, earthenware or metal canisters, or dark-coloured glass. Place them in a cool larder. They will keep their flavour for about six months. Unused herbs which will have lost some of their flavour can be sprinkled round pot plants to keep away insects.

Freezing Herbs

Large leaves, such as those of mint or basil, can be stripped from the cut twigs, frozen separately on trays and stored in sealed polythene bags for up to six months. There is no need to blanch them first. To use, crumble them into cooked dishes. The small leaves of thyme can be treated in the same way.

Large bunches of parsley, and herbs of a similar texture, such as chervil, can be finely chopped before freezing in sealed bags for up to four months. To use, take them out by the spoonful and remember to reseal the bag.

The more delicate herbs, such as dill and fennel, can be chopped and frozen in ice cubes. Three-quarters fill ice-cube trays with the chopped herbs, top up with water and freeze. Store in sealed polythene bags for up to four months. Add the ice cubes to dishes at the beginning of their cooking time.

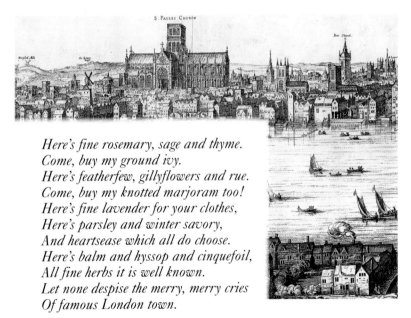

Here's fine rosemary, sage and thyme.
Come, buy my ground ivy.
Here's featherfew, gillyflowers and rue.
Come, buy my knotted marjoram too!
Here's fine lavender for your clothes,
Here's parsley and winter savory,
And heartsease which all do choose.
Here's balm and hyssop and cinquefoil,
All fine herbs it is well known.
Let none despise the merry, merry cries
Of famous London town.

Roxburgh Ballads, 18th century

MEDICAL HERBALISM

MEDICAL HERBALISM IS THE MEDICINAL USE OF PLANTS. IT HAS BEEN PRACTISED FOR AT LEAST

4 MILLION YEARS – AS LONG AS HUMAN BEINGS HAVE BEEN EATING PLANT-BASED FOODS.

A woodcut of a Chinese doctor from the 1850s. The artist wrote, "These doctors always feel the pulses of both wrists. Their medicines consist mostly of herbs."

The first medicinal herbs were probably chosen by instinct and possibly also by a method related to that used to dowse for water. It is interesting to note that the same plants were chosen in many widely separated countries that had no known contact with one another. Treatments are likely to have been discovered on the principle that the craving for certain foods indicated the body's need for them at the time. For example, the strong-flavoured bitter herbs such as dandelion and sorrel were sought out in the spring. We know that these plants contain vitamin C and therefore prevent scurvy – a likely springtime ailment after a limited winter diet. Early healers simply knew that they kept the body healthy.

As human groups became more settled, so medicine became more established. With the advance of cultures came written records of herbs and remedies. In 2800 BC, the Chinese herbalist Shen Nung compiled a list of 366

Many common herbs that are best known for their culinary properties also make effective home remedies.

medicinal herbs, many of which are still used. The ancient Egyptians grew and imported medicinal herbs, which were administered by recognised doctors and by the growers

In ancient Greece, people who grew and supplied herbs were called *rhizotomoki* (root-gatherers), and the earliest Greek herbal, written by Diocles of Carystius in 4 BC, was called *Rhizotomika*. The famous herbal of the Greek physician Dioscorides, published in the 1st century AD, had a profound influence on both Greek and Roman medicine. Armed with its knowledge, physicians followed the Roman legions throughout the Empire, taking their plants with them.

The leading 2nd century physician Galen, doctor to the Roman Emperors, had an influence on medicine that lasted for 1500 years. Some of his remedies were highly complex, and from his time onward a distinction was made between the doctor, who prescribed expensive formulas, and the healer, who used a "specific", a particular herb for one particular effect.

After the Romans, the monks carried on the medical tradition, and there was much inter-action between the monasteries of Europe, with monks of all countries exchanging ideas, remedies and plants. In England, herbal learning was greatly advanced by the later Anglo-Saxons, and in Italy in the 10th century, a medical school based on medical herbalism was founded at Salerno.

Plant cures also featured prominently in Arab medicine, and from the Middle Eastern writer Ibn Said (called Avicenna in the West) came the idea of linking herbal plants with astrology. He believed that each herb was under the influence of or governed by a particular planet.

In early medieval times, both Arab and European medicine became even more complex. Physicians to the rich included pounded gemstones in their remedies in a bid to convince the public that medicines must consist of many expensive ingredients in order to work. Medieval physicians also adopted such practices as

The apothecary diagnosed and treated patients. His cures were based mainly on herbs.

bleeding and blistering which were not abandoned until the middle of the 19th century.

This was the beginning of a medical profession based on expensive chemical cures which, in those early years, probably killed more people than it cured. Ordinary people, however, could not afford physicians. They relied on their own knowledge and the skills of local healers to dispense herbal remedies to their families. Many people grew their own herbs and knew where to find them in the hedgerows, and it was often the duty of the clergyman's wife or the lady of the manor to look after the health of the village. During the 16th and 17th centuries, herbals, such as that of Nicholas Culpeper, were published to help them.

The first European settlers in the New World took their plant remedies with them. In the early years they also acquired a little knowledge about local plants from the native Americans. In the pioneer settlements, home ministering of herbal medicine was much as it had been in Europe.

Being a new country, however, America was open to fresh ideas, and several herbal practitioners, including Samuel Thomson and Wooster Beach, enjoyed recognition and success during the 19th century. Homeopathy

was founded in Germany by Samuel Hahnemann, and the first homeopathy clinic in the United States was opened in New York in 1825 to great acclaim.

In Britain and the rest of Europe, however, most people were turning towards the chemical remedies which were being newly marketed for home treatments. These included previously popular calomel (mercurous chloride), along with plant-based drugs, such as laudanum (a tincture of opium), and purges, such as senna and rhubarb. The plants were used singly, in large quantities, and only to sedate and purge. This is not like gentle herbal medicine which uses relatively small amounts of many different herbs. The seeds of chemical medicine had been sown, and for the first half of the 20th century, medical herbalists struggled for recognition.

In the 1960s the chemical bubble began to burst when fears of side effects spread. In 1977 the World Health Organization started to advocate the use of traditional herbal medicines around the world, and since then proper research has been done into the true benefits of medicinal herbs.

Many people have realised that, for simple common ailments, they can treat themselves with a herbal infusion rather than resorting to expensive chemical pills. With a little herbal knowledge, we can all be our own doctors of physic using plants from our own gardens.

19

In the 15th century, the rich were able to buy expensive and sometimes chemical-based remedies. The poor had to make do with home treatment using their own herbs.

Herbal Treatments in the Home

Herbal remedies such as those to ease a common cold or sore throat, are very easy to make and can work very quickly. Other herbal treatments function slowly and steadily.

For common ailments, simple herbal remedies are ideal. Side effects are few, but those who suffer from a long-term illness, such as a heart complaint, or women who are pregnant should only use herbal treatments under the advice and guidance of a medical practitioner. For serious or persistent illness you should always consult your GP first. With your doctor's approval you should then consult a recommended medical herbalist. There are also many in-depth medical herbals available, which have been written for home use and these should be consulted before self-prescribing.

Buying Herbs for Home Treatment

Always use the highest-quality herbs available. Organically grown herbs from your own herb garden, either fresh or dried, are the best. Alternatively, buy dried herbs from respected suppliers of herbs for medical use. Many of them sell by mail order. Purchase only as much as you need for your course of treatment. Do not keep dried herbs for longer than six months.

Herbal Preparations

Infusion
Put the chopped fresh or dried herb into a container, pour on boiling water, cover and leave for the length of time specified in the remedy. Strain and reserve the liquid.

Decoction
Put the chopped fresh or dried herb into an enamel or stainless-steel saucepan with the amount of water specified in the remedy. Then cover and simmer for the time stated in the recipe. Strain and reserve the liquid.

A herbal infusion is made just like tea, by pouring boiling water over fresh or dried herbs.

Fragrant, culinary and medicinal herbs can be grown in separate areas of the herb garden, although many have dual uses.

Compress
Moisten clean lint in an infusion or decoction and apply it to the affected area. Compresses can be used for bruises, sprains and inflamed areas. If they are required only for a short time, for example up to 15 minutes, they can be held on the affected part by hand; if longer, secure with bandages.

Poultice
Use dried powdered herbs or roots, such as comfrey or marshmallow root. Mix one tablespoon of the powder with a little hot water or hot comfrey infusion to make a paste. Sandwich the hot paste between two pieces of sterile lint and apply it to the affected area.

Tisane
A tisane is an alternative name for an infusion. There is no standard recipe.

Herbal oil
The chopped herb or herb sprigs are put into a screw-top jar or a bottle of oil and covered. The oil is left in a warm place for up to three weeks depending on the recipe and agitated frequently. It is then strained and stored in a clean jar or bottle.

A SELECTION OF HERBAL REMEDIES

Dried herbs are used for many of these remedies. Double the amounts for fresh herbs.

Relief for a Common Cold

There is no cure for a common cold; it has to take its course. But this infusion will bring considerable relief.

2 tbsp dried yarrow
2 tbsp dried elderflowers
1 tbsp dried peppermint
small pinch cayenne pepper
honey for sweetening (optional)

Put the dried herbs and cayenne pepper into a teapot. Pour on 570 ml (20 fl oz) boiling water. Cover, and leave to stand for 5 minutes. Strain and drink hot or warm, over the period of one hour, adding honey to taste if required. This may be repeated twice more during the day.

Remedy for an Upset Stomach

This infusion should settle a stomach that feels queasy in, for example, a case of travel sickness. It will also help to calm the stomach after a period of vomiting.

1 tbsp dried peppermint
¼ tsp fennel seeds

Put the peppermint and fennel seeds into a jug or small teapot. Pour on 285 ml (10 fl oz) boiling water. Cover and leave for 10 minutes. Strain and sip while it is warm.

A Tisane for Sleeplessness

Herbs are gentle sleep inducers. They help you to relax but do not affect your ability to wake up in the morning.

1 tsp dried camomile
1 tsp dried lime (linden) flowers
1 dried hop flower
honey for sweetening

Put the camomile, lime flowers and hop flower into a jug or small teapot. Pour on 285 ml (10 fl oz) boiling water. Cover and leave to infuse for 10 minutes. Strain and sweeten to taste with honey. Relax and sip the tisane slowly.

An Oil for Athlete's Foot

Use a good-quality oil for this. Jojoba or wheatgerm oil can be substituted for almond oil. If these are unavailable, choose a high-quality olive oil. The oils may be purchased from chemists, beauty suppliers and also from some herbalist suppliers. This is a remedy in which fresh herbs work better than dried.

4 tbsp almond oil
1 tbsp chopped fresh thyme leaves

Pour the oil into a small, clear glass container. Add the thyme and cover tightly. Leave the container on a sunny windowsill or in a warm place for one week, shaking every 48 hours. Strain. Apply to the affected area night and morning. If the remedy is for immediate use, put the oil and the thyme into a small saucepan. Heat them very gently, without letting the oil bubble, for 30 minutes. Strain and cool.

A Compress for Bruises

Comfrey is a well-known aid to the fast healing of bruises, sprains and breaks.

2 tbsp dried comfrey
lint large enough to cover the affected area

Put the comfrey and 570 ml (20 fl oz) water into a stainless-steel or enamel saucepan. Bring them gently to the boil, cover and simmer for 30 minutes. Strain. Soak the piece of lint in the decoction, wring it out and apply it, as hot as possible without burning, to the affected area.

A Warm Mouthwash to ease Toothache

This infusion will ease the pain of toothache, but will not get rid of the cause. It is best to consult a dentist as soon as possible.

1 tsp dried red sage (or common sage if red is unavailable)
1 clove

Put the sage and clove into a jug. Pour on 200 ml (7 fl oz) boiling water. Cover and leave until it is warm. Strain and use as a mouthwash immediately. Any remaining mouthwash can be kept covered in the refrigerator for up to two days.

Aromatic Herbs

The scents of herbs can be refreshing, relaxing, healing and sensuous. Sitting or walking in a fragrant herb garden can ease stressed minds, and herbal scents have long been used to combat disease, repel insects and even keep away evil spirits.

If a room is pervaded with an underlying sweet scent of herbs it improves everyone's well-being. The ancient Egyptians were the first to show interest in the aromatic properties of herbs. They made scented unguents for their bodies and created pots-pourris by burying large crocks of scented rose petals in the ground to assist fermentation. There are frequent mentions of herbs in both the Bible and the Koran; the Song of Songs gives thanks for "all things good, even pleasant smells for our noses".

The Greeks planted fragrant herb gardens around their houses, believing that the sweet sharp scents would keep the household healthy. The Romans hung up bunches of herbs to deter insects, scattered rose petals over banqueting floors and scented their communal baths with rosemary. All manner of sweet-smelling herbs were planted in symbolic patterns in Arab gardens of the early medieval period, to be used for perfuming the body and surrounding environment. The Crusaders learned from the Arabs and returned home with ideas for fragrant gardens, perfumes and for scenting houses. The custom began of strewing the floors of churches and living rooms with aromatic herbs which gave out their scent as they were crushed underfoot.

It was in the 16th century that the use of fragrant herbs in the home became really popular throughout Europe. Larger houses had a still-room where women made pots-pourris, pomanders and sweet bags for linen, and where they distilled the essence of flowers and herbs for perfumes and washing waters. Those with no space for a still-room worked at the kitchen table. Scented herbal preparations became essential deodorisers in houses with small, high windows, beaten mud floors and no dampcourse.

The art of the still-room was taken to the United States and employed as soon as settlements became established and peaceful. It began to die out in the 19th century in countries such as Britain when industrialization caused a move to the towns; but in country districts it remained popular until the beginning of the 20th century. It never entirely disappeared, however, and there is now a revival of interest. You can buy pot-pourri and natural fragrances in many shops; and with a selection of scented herbs and a few additional ingredients you can make your scented preparations.

Herbs in Pots and Bunches

Bringing a pot containing a fragrant herb, such as rosemary, into the house is the simplest way of scenting a room, and was often recommended in the 16th century.

Hanging up a bunch of herbs was a Roman idea which can easily be employed today. This not only scents the room but can also keep away insects. Use the following herbs singly or in any mixtures that please you.

To freshen the air: lavender, rosemary, santolina (cotton lavender), hyssop, mint, thyme, woodruff.

To cool the air: lavender, rosemary, wormwood, woodruff.

To deter flies: rue, tansy, pennyroyal, peppermint, basil.

Pot-pourri

A pot-pourri is a fragrant mixture of dried herbs and flowers which is kept in a perforated container or open bowl in a place where its scent can perfume a room.

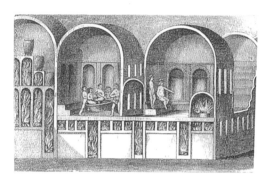

The Romans scented their baths with herbal extracts and used herbal oils for perfume and massage.

A 15th-century German woodcut showing a wattle garden with roses.

The original method of making a pot-pourri, devised by the ancient Egyptians, was to bury a crock of sweet-scented leaves and petals in the ground so that the contents fermented and eventually became a dry, highly aromatic mixture. This technique gave pot-pourri its name which, translated literally from the French, means "rotten pot". It was employed by the Greeks, Romans and Arabs, and was the method used in 16th-century still-rooms.

This traditional way of making pot-pourri is known today as the "moist" method. It takes a long time and you need a great many fresh flowers, but the result is a mixture with a strong, sweet fragrance that will last five years or more.

The "dry" method of making pot-pourri is much simpler, and this is the best means to choose if you have more aromatic herbs than flowers. You can grow herbs specially for a dry pot-pourri. You can also use a large proportion of culinary herbs. Many herbs have to be cut back in the summer, and it would be impossible to use them all in the kitchen, so making a pot-pourri is an excellent means of ensuring that they are not wasted. All herbs and flowers for a dry pot-pourri should be dried until they are crisp. If you are unable to grow your own herbs and flowers, many of those listed below can be bought dried from herbalists.

HERBS FOR DRY POT-POURRI: Agrimony, bay, clary sage, costmary (alecost), leaves of scented geraniums (e.g. mint or lemon), lavender, lemon balm, lemon verbena, marjoram, mints of various sorts (eau de Cologne mint, apple mint, spearmint, bergamot mint), pennyroyal, pineapple sage, santolina (cotton lavender), southernwood, tansy, thyme (common and other fragrant thymes), woodruff, wormwood.

FLOWERS FOR DRY POT-POURRI: Rose petals, carnations, honeysuckle, heliotrope, jasmin, orange blossom, peony, stocks, violets, wall-flowers. You can also add some flowers purely for their colour, such as borage, cornflower, hibiscus, larkspur, marigolds, nasturtiums, salvia and zinnias.

OTHER INGREDIENTS: These include spices, woods and the dried peels of citrus fruits, which are added in small quantities. Spices are best bought whole and crushed with a pestle and mortar just before you add them.

FIXATIVES: These help to preserve the scent of a pot-pourri. Orris-root powder is the most popular and readily available. It is the dried, ground root of *Iris florentina*.

ESSENTIAL OILS: These heighten the scent of a dry pot-pourri. Choose oils that match your herbs (for example, use lavender oil if there is a large proportion of lavender in the mixture), and add only a drop at a time, because you will need very little. Essential oils for pot-pourri can be bought from herbalists, chemists and health food stores.

Hanged up in houses, it [woodruff] doth very well attemper the aire, coole and make fresh the place to the delight and comfort of such as are therein.

JOHN GERARD, 1596

Herbal Pot-Pourri

This is a pot-pourri with a fresh, clean scent, made with a selection of fragrant herbs that are common in most herb gardens.

45 g • 1½ oz lavender
30 g • 1 oz hyssop
30 g • 1 oz marjoram or oregano
15 g • ½ oz thyme
15 g • ½ oz eau de Cologne mint or peppermint
cinnamon sticks together measuring 25 cm • 10 in
½ nutmeg, freshly grated
30 g • 1 oz orris-root powder
4 drops lavender oil

Dry all the herbs completely (until crisp). Then mix the dried herbs together in a bowl. Crush the cinnamon sticks with a pestle and mortar or grind them between two sheets of greaseproof paper with a rolling pin. Add them to the herbs. Add the nutmeg and orris-root powder and mix well. Add the lavender oil, stirring after each drop. Put the pot-pourri in a polythene bag, seal the top and leave it for one month. Transfer it to a jar or bowl for display.

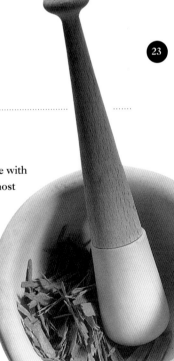

COLGATE & CO's
CASHMERE BOUQUET
PERFUME
for the Handkerchief

CASHMERE BOUQUET
is composed of the most fragrant and costly extracts from flowers
Each bottle bears the name and trade mark of
COLGATE & CO.
Soap Makers
and Perfumers,
NEW YORK.

BASIC METHOD: Select the herbs and flowers that will determine the basic scent of the pot-pourri; then choose others to complement them. Mix them together and sniff. Add spices and woods to balance the overall effect. Mix again. Add essential oil, one drop at a time, mixing and testing the scent after each addition. Put the finished pot-pourri into a polythene bag and seal the top. Leave it for one month to allow the fragrance to blend and mature.

CONTAINERS FOR POT-POURRI: A pot-pourri in an open bowl will scent the room strongly for about a month, after which the scent will diminish. If you keep it in a lidded bowl and remove the lid only when needed, the scent will last longer. Whichever container you choose, stir the pot-pourri once a day to release the scent and to prevent the top layer from losing its smell completely.

SWEET BAGS

Sweet bags are fabric sachets containing dried herb mixtures which can be placed among clothes or in a linen cupboard, on a dressing table or on a chair. Lavender has always been the favourite herb for sweet bags because of its fresh, clean scent and its ability to repel moths. Other moth deterring herbs are rosemary, cotton lavender (santolina), thyme, woodruff, southernwood and wormwood. Use them singly or mixed, and add 1 teaspoon of orris-root powder for every 30 g (1 oz) of dried herbs. Crushed cloves, or cinnamon, or small pieces of nutmeg can be added. For making

. . . in summer, the chimney fireplace be trimmed with a bank of fresh moss and at either end have a rosemary pot.

SIR HUGH PLATT, *DELIGHTS FOR LADIES*, 1594

A 19th-century advertisement for James Floris, a London perfumer, who sold herbal aromatic vinegars and perfumes.

sweet bags, choose a natural-fibre material, such as cotton, silk or linen, with a fairly tight weave. Decorate the bags with frills, ribbons or lace and sew on loops for hanging.

As a guide, 30 g (1 oz) herb mixture will fill a rectangular sachet that measures approximately 10 x 15 cm (4 x 6 in).

BURNING PERFUMES

The word perfume comes from the Latin *per* ("through") and *fumare* ("to smoke"), so to perfume a room in Roman times was to refresh it with pleasantly scented smoke. The simplest way of doing this, and probably the oldest, is to place fragrant herb sprigs on the embers of a fire. Lavender, rosemary, angelica seeds, southernwood and bay leaves are the most suitable.

From the 11th to the 18th century, when rush mats and beds harboured fleas, burning wormwood and rue in the room was found to be an effective and aromatic repellent. American Indians burned bunches of herbs, known as

Lemon and Lavender Sweet Bag Mixture

This has a fresh, clean scent and is suitable for putting in a drawer amongst clothes, or in the linen cupboard. Orris-root powder is the powdered root of the Florentine iris. It is available from herbalists.

30 g • 1 oz lemon verbena
30 g • 1 oz lavender
30 g • 1 oz hyssop (if available)
1 tsp ground nutmeg
1 tbsp dried orris-root powder

smudge sticks, for rituals and for purification, and these can also be used in the home. The herbs, often a variety of different sages, are bound tightly together to form a candle shape. When lit, they smoulder gently, emitting a delicious scent. They can be extinguished in water, then dried and relit when needed. Smudge sticks, sometimes called sage brushes, are available from specialist shops.

One step on from scattering herbs on the fire was to heat them in a chafing dish, similar to a frying pan, which was filled with sweet-smelling herbs and spices and set over hot coals. Keep an old frying pan for this purpose and heat the herbs on the hob over a low heat. It is an excellent way of getting rid of cooking smells.

Queen Anne's Chafing Dish

85 ml • 3 fl oz rose-water
2 tsp fresh rosemary leaves
2 cloves
½ tsp sugar

Put all the ingredients into a small frying pan and simmer them over a low heat until the liquid has almost evaporated. Do not let the liquid boil away completely or the pan will burn.

ANNE.

Herb Candles

This is a basic method for making 425 ml (15 fl oz) of herb-scented wax. The specialist equipment and ingredients can be bought from candlemakers' suppliers.

EQUIPMENT
One or more plastic, glass or metal moulds together totalling the volume given (herbs may damage rubber moulds)
sunflower oil for greasing moulds
wick (use a thicker wick for wider candles)
wicking needle
mould seal
cocktail sticks
double saucepan or bowl to stand in a saucepan of water
old small saucepan
thermometer (ordinary or specialist candle-making one may be used)

INGREDIENTS
340 g • 12 oz paraffin wax
35 g • 1¼ oz stearin
⅛ tsp finely grated dye disc (green, blue, purple or whatever colour suits your herb - optional)
30 g • 1 oz dried herbs (e.g. lavender, rosemary, thyme, hyssop)

METHOD
Lightly grease the moulds. Using the wicking needle, pull the wick through the hole in the top of the mould. The length of wick used will depend on the size of mould used. Secure the wick with mould seal at the top end. Tie it to a cocktail stick at the other end, so that it stays taut through the mould. Place the moulds upside down in a holder. Moulds often come with their own holder, or alternatively you could improvise with another container suitable for the size and shape of the mould. Thin candles could be stuck into plasticine. Melt the wax in a double saucepan and heat gently to a temperature of 75°C (185°F). Melt the stearin and grated dye disc in a small saucepan. Add them to the wax.

Stir in the herbs.

Pour the mixture into the moulds, distributing the herbs evenly between them. Leave the wax for 10 minutes.

If depressions appear in the surface, top up with any remaining wax in the saucepan. Leave for 5 hours or until the candles are completely set.

To remove the candles from the moulds, pull gently on the cocktail stick, using it as a lever. If the candles appear to be stuck (the presence of herbs in the wax sometimes has this effect), dip the moulds briefly into hot water.

Trim the wicks.

NOTE: The herbs will probably not remain evenly distributed throughout the candles. Some sink to the bottom, others float in the wax. This does not detract from the finished appearance.

HERB DIRECTORY

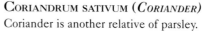

ALLIUM SATIVUM (*GARLIC*)

Garlic is a perennial plant with a flattened round bulb, made up of eight to ten sections called cloves, held together by a thin papery covering. The cloves have a savoury, pungent flavour. Culinary, medicinal, cosmetic.

ALLIUM SCHOENOPRASUM (*CHIVES*)

Chives are a relative of the onion. They are perennial plants which produce thin, hollow leaves from March to October. They have a mild onion flavour. Culinary.

ANETHUM GRAVEOLENS (*DILL*)

Dill is an annual plant which has delicate feathery leaves and a rich flavour. In temperate climates it can be picked throughout the summer. The seeds are also used. Culinary, medicinal.

ARTEMISIA DRACUNCULUS (*TARRAGON*)

Tarragon is a perennial plant which dies back completely in winter and which can be picked from late spring until early autumn. Its flavour is warming, spicy and slightly sweet. Culinary, medicinal.

BORAGO OFFICINALIS (*BORAGE*)

Borage is a tall perennial plant which has large, hairy leaves and small blue and black flowers that can be picked from early summer to early autumn. It has a cucumber-like flavour. Both its leaves and flowers are used. Culinary, medicinal.

CHAEROPHYLLUM SATIVUM (*CHERVIL*)

Chervil is an annual from the same family as parsley, and has delicate, deeply cut leaves. Its flavour contains a hint of liquorice. It can be cut in the spring, and again in the early autumn and after summer seeding. Culinary, medicinal.

CORIANDRUM SATIVUM (*CORIANDER*)

Coriander is another relative of parsley. It is an annual, with flat, wide, toothed leaves. It has a sweet, pungent flavour. The seeds are also used. Culinary, medicinal, cosmetic.

ERUCA SATIVA (*ROCKET*)

Rocket is a perennial plant which grows in long, leafy stems. It has a slightly hot, peppery flavour. Culinary.

FOENICULUM VULGARE (*FENNEL*)

Fennel is a tall perennial plant with large, feathery leaves, which gradually fall backwards as they grow. Its flavour is reminiscent of aniseed. The seeds are also used. Culinary, medicinal.

LAURUS NOBILIS (*BAY*)

The bay is an evergreen tree which flourishes in tubs and in sheltered areas. The leaves, which are the part used, are of a pointed oval shape and shiny on the uppermost side. Bay has a slightly bitter, savoury flavour. Culinary, medicinal, aromatic.

LAVANDULA ANGUSTIFOLIA (*LAVENDER*)

Lavender is a low, shrubby bush, with narrow, pointed, grey-green leaves and spikes of purple flowers. It has a sweet, sharp, pungent flavour. Culinary, medicinal, aromatic, cosmetic.

LEVISTUCUM OFFICINALE (*LOVAGE*)

Lovage is a tall, perennial plant, which has large, serrated leaves. The leaves can be picked throughout the summer. Its flavour is reminiscent of hot, spicy celery. Culinary, medicinal.

MELISSA OFFICINALIS (*LEMON BALM*)

Lemon balm is a bushy, perennial plant, which has heart-shaped leaves growing on long spikes, topped with whorls of small white flowers. The leaves can be picked from late spring to early autumn.

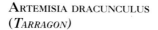

The flavour is a combination of spice, honey and lemon. Culinary, medicinal, aromatic, cosmetic.

MENTHA SPICATA (*SPEARMINT*)

There are many varieties of mint, the most common being *M. spicata*, or spearmint. All mints are perennial plants which spread rapidly. The oval, pointed leaves have a refreshing flavour and can be picked throughout the summer. Culinary, medicinal, cosmetic.

OCYMUM BASILICUM (*BASIL*)

Basil is a delicate annual plant which loves the sun and is usually harvested only in the summer months. Its bright green leaves grow from a central stem topped with spikes of white flowers. The flavour is pungent, sweet and slightly spicy. Culinary, medicinal.

ORIGANUM MARJORANA (*SWEET MARJORAM*)

Sweet marjoram is one of the may varieties of marjoram. It is a perennial plant which can be picked from spring until autumn. It has small, oval leaves, growing on the main and branching stems, and a savoury-sweet flavour. Culinary, medicinal, aromatic.

ORIGANUM VULGARE (*OREGANO OR WILD MARJORAM*)

Similar in appearance and habit to marjoram, oregano has a spicier flavour. Culinary.

PETROSELINUM SATIVUM (*PARSLEY*)

Parsley is probably the most used of all herbs. It is an annual plant with a generous supply of curled, bright green leaves and a mild, savoury flavour. It can be picked from spring to autumn. Culinary, medicinal, cosmetic.

ROSMARINUS OFFICINALIS (*ROSEMARY*)

Rosemary is a perennial, shrubby bush. Its small, spiked leaves, dark green on one side and grey-green on the other, can be picked throughout the year. The scent and flavour of rosemary is strong

and pungent. Culinary, medicinal, aromatic, cosmetic.

RUMEX SCUTATUS (*SORREL*)

The garden variety of sorrel is *R. scutatus*. It is a perennial plant with large, spinach-like leaves which are often wrinkled and tall spikes of red flowers. The leaves have a very sharp, fresh flavour and it is at its best in the spring and early summer. Culinary, medicinal.

SALVIA OFFICINALIS (*SAGE*)

Sage is a perennial, shrubby bush with tongue-shaped, grey-green leaves and purple flowers. It can be gathered all year but is at its best in spring and summer. The flavour is slightly spicy and savoury. Culinary, medicinal.

SATUREJA MONTANA/HORTENSIS (*SAVORY*)

A small, woody, evergreen shrub, *S. montana* has little, spiky leaves and a warming, spicy flavour. *S. hortensis*, or summer savory, is a perennial, more delicate in flavour and texture. Culinary.

TARAXACUM OFFICINALE (*DANDELION*)

The dandelion is a wild plant which can also be cultivated. It is perennial, but its long, toothed leaves are best in spring when they are tender and delicately flavoured. Culinary, medicinal, cosmetic.

THYMUS VULGARIS (*COMMON THYME*)

Thyme is a low-growing perennial plant with tiny leaves and purple flowers. There are many different varieties but *T. vulgaris* is the most widely used. Thyme has a savoury-sweet flavour. Culinary, medicinal, aromatic.

URTICA DIOICA (*NETTLE*)

The nettle is a wild, perennial plant which grows prolifically. Its heart-shaped, serrated leaves should be picked in the spring when they are young. Nettles have a savoury flavour more like a vegetable than a herb. Culinary, medicinal, cosmetic.

HERBAL BEAUTY

FROM EARLIEST TIMES, HERBS HAVE BEEN USED TO ENHANCE BEAUTY. THEY ARE STILL REGARDED AS EFFECTIVE COSMETICS, AND THEY ARE CERTAINLY THE SAFEST. MANY NOT ONLY CONTAIN INGREDIENTS TO IMPROVE THE CONDITION OF THE SKIN AND HAIR, BUT ALSO POSSESS ATTRACTIVE SCENTS.

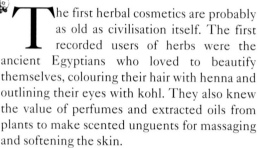

The first herbal cosmetics are probably as old as civilisation itself. The first recorded users of herbs were the ancient Egyptians who loved to beautify themselves, colouring their hair with henna and outlining their eyes with kohl. They also knew the value of perfumes and extracted oils from plants to make scented unguents for massaging and softening the skin.

From Roman times onwards, women regarded pale-coloured faces as beautiful and lightened their complexions by bathing their faces with a mixture of honey, lemon juice and herbal infusions. A face-pack to make the skin paler and soothe away wrinkles was invented in the 1st century AD by the Roman naturalist Pliny. It contained ground peas (or barley), egg white, honey, wine and a secretion from narcissus bulbs. In the 17th century, Queen Henrietta Maria of England used a mixture of apricot paste and orange-flower water for the same purpose.

In 1370, Queen Elizabeth of Hungary ordered the making of a face lotion which she claimed would give the user a wrinkle-free face long into old age. The recipe, said to have been given to her by a monk, came to be called Hungary Water, and its main ingredients were rosemary and lavender. Carmelite Water,

Venus, Roman goddess of love and beauty.

Elderflower Facial Scrub

This is a very gentle exfoliant which will remove the upper layer of dead cells to leave your skin feeling soft, smooth and vibrant. It is suitable for all skin types.

1 tbsp dried elderflowers
85 ml • 3 fl oz boiling water
2 tbsp fine oatmeal

Put the elderflowers into a bowl or jug and pour on the boiling water. Cover and leave to infuse until cold, then strain.
Put the oatmeal into a bowl and mix in 3 tablespoons of the elderflower infusion. Gently massage the mixture into your face, for about 5 minutes.
Remove the scrub with tepid water. Pat your face dry with a soft towel and apply a toner and moisturiser.

Marjoram is one of the herbs that can be used for a scented bath. Besides adding fragrance, it can relieve aching muscles.

Hungary Water

Take to every gallon of brandy or clean Spirits, one handful of Rosemary, one handful of Lavender. I suppose the handfuls to be about a foot long a-piece; and these herbs must be cut in pieces about an Inch long. Put these to infuse in the Spirits, and with them, about one handful of Myrtle, cut as before. When this has stood three days, distil it, and you will have the finest Hungary Water that can be.

R. BRADLEY, *THE COUNTRY HOUSEWIFE AND LADY'S DIRECTOR*, 1732

28

Fragrant camomile has a tautening and cleansing effect on the face, and it has long been used as a rinse to bring out highlights in blonde hair.

containing lemon balm and angelica, and first made in 1379 by nuns of the Abbey of St Just, France, also became popular with noble-women throughout medieval Europe.

Beauty, cleanliness and fragrance have always gone together, and the simplest cosmetics of the past were sweet washing waters. These were produced by the infusion, decoction (boiling), or distillation of sweetly scented flowers and herbs, to extract their essence. It is said that the first rose-water was made by the Arab physician Avicenna in the 10th century, but it was probably in use long before that, even though it went out of fashion in the Dark Ages. In medieval times, elaborate jars of rose-water were placed on the tables of the rich for diners to rinse their fingers and refresh their clothes. There were no forks in those days, and eating could be a messy business.

Rose-water remained popular for centuries. Waters made with rosemary, marjoram, lavender, basil, pennyroyal and costmary were used for the same purpose; up until the 19th century, jugs of washing water in the guest bedroom were scented with herbs.

It is also well to boil the flowers and leaves [of rosemary] in water and to wash yourself therewith every morning, omitting to dry it with a cloth, but leaving it to do so naturally. By washing thus with perseverance, the aged will retain a youthful look as long as they live.

QUOTED BY MRS C.F. LEYEL IN *THE MAGIC OF HERBS*, 1926

Herb-scented baths had been popular with the Egyptians, Greeks and Romans, but bathing fell out of favour after the collapse of the Roman Empire and was not a frequent occurrence again until the 17th century. Then various herbs were added to the bath water to soften and scent the skin. In rich households, milk and oatmeal were used to increase the softening effects.

Beautiful hair has always been coveted and herbs have long been used to maintain a good head of hair. Rosemary and nettle, camomile and sage have been the most popular hair treatments. People have lightened their hair with camomile and rhubarb, coloured it red with henna and darkened it with sage. These herbs are still used today.

Parsley Face Mask

Like the facial scrub, this face mask will gently exfoliate the skin, getting rid of dead skin cells and speeding up the renewal process. Parsley leaves your skin feeling refreshed and is suitable for all skin types.

2 tbsp chopped fresh parsley
4 tbsp cornmeal
2–3 tbsp natural yoghurt

Put the parsley and cornmeal into a bowl and mix in 2 tablespoons of the yoghurt. You should be able to spread the mixture easily, so if the mask is on the dry side, add up to 1 tablespoon more of the yoghurt.
Spread the mixture over your face, avoiding the area immediately around the eyes. Lie down and relax for 15 minutes.
Rinse the mask off with tepid water. Pat your face dry with a soft towel and then apply a toner and moisturiser.

29

Herbal Hair Rinse

The most effective herbs for healthy, shining hair are rosemary and nettles, and both can be used as a base for rinses to revive your hair. Rosemary is best for general use and nettles are good for hair that has dried out in the sun.

30 g • 1 oz dried rosemary or fresh nettle leaves
570 ml • 1 pint boiling water
oil of lavender, lemon or orange (for nettle leaves only)

Put the herb into a jug or bowl. Pour on the boiling water, cover and leave to infuse for 2 hours. Line a sieve with muslin or a coffee filter paper and strain the rinse through it. If you are using nettles, add 4 drops of your chosen oil to improve the scent, and mix well. The rinse will keep in a cool place for up to a day.
To use, wash and thoroughly rinse your hair in the normal way. Then with your head over a basin, slowly pour the herb rinse through your hair, making sure that it reaches every part. Gently massage the rinse into your hair. Towel dry and for maximum effect leave your hair to finish drying naturally.

Herb	Effect	Skin type
Camomile	Tautening, cleansing, lightening hair colour, anti-inflammatory	all
Comfrey	Emollient, healing	all
Elderflower	Cleansing, lightening hair colour, emollient	all
Fennel	Cleansing, gentle astringent	all
Lavender	Antiseptic, stimulating	all
Lemon balm	Tautening	all
Lime flower	Tautening	all
Marigold	Cleansing, mildly astringent, healing	all
Mint	Strong astringent, spot cleanser	not for sensitive skins
Nettle	Cleansing, purifying, toning	all
Parsley	Cleansing, toning, helps combat thread veins	all
Rosemary	Tautening	all
Sage	Astringent, cooling	oily
Thyme	Toning, refreshing, antiseptic	all
Violet	Emollient, cleansing	dry
Woodruff	For soreness after exposure to sun or wind	all
Yarrow	Astringent	oily

MAKING HERBAL COSMETICS

Herbal cosmetics are easy to make at home. The ingredients are readily available – you probably have many of them in your kitchen already. For most cosmetics, you will need only simple equipment, such as spoons, bowls or sieves. Be sure to clean these well before and after making cosmetics. If you intend to create your own beauty treatments regularly, it is worthwhile keeping a separate set of implements purely for that purpose.

HERBS TO USE

The most frequently used cosmetic herbs are listed left. You can grow your own, obtain them fresh from sources that sell herbs for food, or buy them dried, direct or by mail order, from reputable herb suppliers.

Some herbs suit all skin types. Others are either astringent, which means that they have a drying effect, or emollient, which means that they contain materials that form gels when mixed with water which soften the skin. Use astringent herbs for oily skin and emollient herbs for dry skin. Other effects produced by herbs are tautening (making your skin feel smoother and tighter), and soothing or healing.

Buttermilk and Lime Flower Cleanser

This is a very gentle cleanser, suitable for all skin types.

285 ml • 10 fl oz cultured buttermilk
4 tbsp lime flowers
2 tbsp honey

Put the buttermilk and lime flowers into a saucepan. Bring them to simmering point, cover the pan and keep it on the lowest temperature possible for 30 minutes. Remove from the heat and stir in the honey. Cover again and leave for 2 hours. Strain and bottle the cleanser. Store it in the refrigerator and use within 1 week. Use to cleanse the face of grime or of light make-up.

Herbal Skin Toner

A toner splashed on to the face after cleansing will help to close the pores and invigorate the skin. The only ingredients you need are fresh or dried herbs and still, bottled spring water. Choose the herbs from the list on page 30.

30 g • 1 oz fresh herbs or 15 g • ½ oz dried
285 ml • 10 fl oz still spring water

Put the herbs into a jug. Boil the water and pour it over the herbs. Cover with clingfilm or a lid and leave to infuse for 2 hours.
Line a sieve with muslin or coffee filter paper and strain the infusion through it. Store the toner in a covered jar in the refrigerator and use within a week.

Rosemary was one of the essential herbal ingredients of Hungary water. Use it for a herbal skin toner, a mouthwash or in a rinse for your hair.

Mrs C.F. Leyel, 1880–1957

Mrs Leyel was the daughter of a housemaster at Uppingham School, Rutland, in England, where her interest in flowers and herbs developed.
She intended to study medicine, but withdrew when faced with her first dissection, and instead joined a theatre company and married a theatrical manager.
Attractive and vivacious, she was much involved in London society, but she maintained her passion for herbs and their uses.
When she became a widow in the 1920s, she began writing about herbs, and her many books include The Magic of Herbs, Herbal Delights, The Truth About Herbs *and* The Gentle Art of Cookery. *She also built up a vast collection of old herbals. In 1929, on the death of Maud Grieve, she brought together and collated Mrs Grieve's pamphlets on herbs to produce "A Modern Herbal" which was published in 1931.*
In 1927 Mrs Leyel opened the first of her shops, Culpeper House in Baker Street, London, selling herbal cosmetics, foods and medicines. This was the start of the Culpeper chain, which continues today.
Mrs Leyel also founded the Society of Herbalists, and

successfully fought for its existence when it was threatened by the Pharmacy and Medicines Bill of 1941, which would have outlawed the practice of medical herbalism.

"THE LEAVES OF THE TREE ARE FOR THE HEALING OF THE NATIONS"

Inside Mrs Leyel's first shop, Culpeper House, opened in Baker Street, London, in 1927.

CULINARY HERBS

HERBS IMPROVE FLAVOUR AND CONTAIN HEALTH-GIVING MINERALS, VITAMINS AND TRACE ELEMENTS.

THEY PROVIDE A WIDE VARIETY OF TASTE FOR BOTH SAVOURY AND SWEET DISHES.

The first human beings were hunter-gatherers; they hunted wild animals and gathered plant foods. By trial and error they discovered how each plant tasted, whether it could be eaten in quantity or whether it was better to scatter one or two leaves over fire-cooked meat. They also found out which herbs suited which meats, not only in terms of flavour but also to improve digestibility.

By the time earthenware cooking pots were in use around 10000 BC, cereal and vegetable stews were the basic diet in many parts of the world. Salt was scarce and sharp-tasting green plants were used to give extra flavour. They also supplied important vitamin C in seasons when there was no wild fruit. In Europe the herbs most often used at this time were nettles, plantain, mallows, docks, ramsons (wild garlic), wild leeks and chives. Thick stews, cooked in a pot over an open fire, remained the main food of the ordinary people for many centuries, becoming known much later as pottages.

In medieval times the most common dish in ordinary households was pottage flavoured with green herbs, including orache (Atriplex, or goosefoot), clary (a type of mint), mallow, dock and bugloss (borage), plus the sage, parsley, thyme, mints and fennel we would recognise today. A pottage that was coloured green with the many herbs used was called *joutes*. It was also sometimes eaten as a sauce.

By the 17th century, the large-leaved wild herbs, such as mallow and bugloss, gave way to new vegetables, such as spinach, and only country people collected nettles and turnip tops. French cookery books began to recommend mixtures of what they called "sweet" or "fine" herbs, which meant the herbs of mainly Mediterranean origin that we would regard as culinary herbs today. They included thyme, marjoram, oregano, basil, rosemary, savory, parsley and sage. The French recommendations influenced cooks all over Europe and, particularly after the Restoration, English cookery books began to give the instruction "take a faggot of sweet herbs".

Sage has long been known as a herb for rich meats, both to add flavour and to make them more digestible.

32

In medieval times a great quantity of meat was eaten in rich households. Large amounts of herbs and spices were used to disguise its flavour when it was not very fresh.

Salua

Nautre. c. q. b. i. z. melior exca comestica. Juuamenium paralesi. et neruis. nocumentum. vitiugat capilos. remotio nocumen. cum lesiuis in quo sit mixt. a civi orientalis.

Joutes

Take borage, violet, mallows, parsley, young worts, beet, avens, bugloss, with orache and others, pick them clean, and cast them on a vessel, and boyl them a good while; then take them and presse them on a fair board, and hew them right small, and put white bread thereto, and grind withal; and then cast them into a fair pot, and [pour in] good fresh broth enough thereto through a strainer.

15TH-CENTURY MANUSCRIPT

Spices such as nutmeg became more readily available in Europe by the mid-18th century. For a time the use of mace and nutmeg almost replaced herbs completely.

By the mid-18th century, thick pottages, made with a mixture of both small and large leaved plants, had virtually disappeared and cooks relied on the "sweet herbs" for most of their dishes. Spices became more readily available and spices such as mace and nutmeg often replaced herbs completely. In the 18th century there was a vogue for making bottled sauces, which were kept in the kitchen ready for use as instant flavourings and in gravies.

In the 19th century, the same "sweet herbs" were being referred to by some cooks as "savoury herbs". In England, they were put into stuffings, sauces and soups and occasionally into salads, but interest in them was waning. Mrs Beeton, writing in 1891, appears not to have been enthusiastic about herbs, and in the United States Fanny Farmer's cook book uses them even less. Bottled sauces and a flavouring called Poultry Seasoning seem to have been the order of the day. In France and other European countries, such as Spain and Italy, herbs were used far more generously and they were always popular.

That remained the case until the 1960s. By then there were so many commercial foods containing artificial flavourings on the market that people began to realise they were missing the natural taste and the health-giving qualities of fresh herbs. This lack of taste became more obvious as people increasingly travelled abroad and sampled the cuisine of other countries. The foods, flavourings and seasonings of ethnic minorities have spilled over from specialist shops and markets to become common ingredients available to everyone. Herbs have once again become essential components of our diet.

A powdering mill used in New York kitchens in the 1850s for reducing herbs and roots into powdered form.

Green Dumplings: Mrs Lord's Receipt

Slice a pound of the crume (crumb) of browne bread, then haveing your pott boyleing with beef scume off ye fatt and put to it ye bread in which let it soake an houre, then beate it with a spoone very small, then put in 5 eggs whites and all and a little ginger and sweet herbs shred small, whereof tow parts must be penneroyall stir it all together and strew in flower with three quarters of a pound of suet cutt very small; then haveing a little flower rubed one ye palmes of ye hands role them rounde and put them into ye pott when it boyls very fast three quarters of an howre boyles them.

HERBS IN THE KITCHEN

To FLAVOUR OR GARNISH FOOD, HERBS CAN BE USED WHOLE,

AS SPRIGS OR LEAVES, OR CHOPPED.

When preparing fresh herbs, cut sprigs from the plant carefully with sharp scissors; rinse the sprigs in cold water and shake them dry. If you are using whole leaves – as a garnish, for example – choose the most attractive ones from the plant.

When chopping herbs, whether you can use or discard the stems depends on the herb. For shrubby herbs with woody stems, such as thyme, winter savory or rosemary, it is best to remove the stems completely. Small, hard pieces of stem are unpleasant in any dish. Where the stems are soft, as in parsley or chervil, you can chop the tops of the stems with the leaves. In all cases, you should have more leaf than stem.

To chop herbs you need a sharp, heavy chopping knife, or a mezzaluna, and a chopping board. For a large-leaved herb, begin by holding the leaves together with one hand and slicing with the other. Once the pieces are

A basket of thyme and freshly cut fennel, rosemary, mint and parsley, ready for cooking aromatic dishes in the kitchen.

small enough, hold the knife blade with both hands and chop quickly and sharply over the herb until it is finely chopped.

BOUQUET GARNI

A bouquet garni is made from a selection of herbs tied together. It is used to flavour dishes such as soups and stews as they cook. Choose the herbs to suit the other ingredients of the dish; for example, a sprig each of parsley, thyme and marjoram for a chicken casserole. Add a bay leaf or a small strip of leek. Tie the bouquet together with fine cotton string, leaving a loop long enough to hold it by. Put the bouquet garni into a dish such as a casserole, soup or braised dish and remove it before serving.

USES OF HERBS

Herbs will add extra flavour and interest to a wide variety of dishes from soups to desserts. See below for suggestions of how to use herbs with each dish.

SOUPS: Add a bouquet garni to the soup at the beginning of cooking time, and remove it before blending if the soup is to be a smooth one or before serving if not. Garnish the soup with chopped herbs.

CASSEROLES, STEWS AND BRAISED DISHES: Flavour with chopped herbs or a bouquet garni while

To make a coole tankett [tankard] – take a quart of Renish wine, or whitewine and put to it a pinte of fayre water, and 2 Lemmons, sweeten it to your likeing with good suger, and put on it some Burage [borage], Baume [lemon balm], and Burnett, if you please. Let ye Lemmon pill be cutt hansomely some to be in ye wine and some to hang on ye tankett.

REBECCA PRICE, 17TH CENTURY

Costmary Conserve

Pick the flowers when they are dry, only use the petals, weigh them and to every pound of petals take two pounds and a half of loaf sugar. Beat the two together in a stone mortar, adding the sugar by degrees. When well incorporated, press into gallipots without first boiling. Tie over paper and leather on top of the paper and it will keep seven years.

HANNAH GLASSE, 1747

Parsley

The excellency of this herb accordeth with the frequent use thereof. For there is almost no meat or sauce which will not have Perseley either in it or about it.

<small>FROM DYET'S *DRY DINNER*, 1599</small>

The delicate appearance of chives gives a clue to their gentle, onion-like flavour. Fresh chives can be picked from March to October.

The beautiful, feathery leaves of dill have a strong, pungent aroma. They often give flavour to cucumber pickles and to Gravad Lax, the Scandinavian dish of raw, marinated salmon.

cooking. Garnish with chopped herbs before serving.

ROASTS: Lay sprigs of herbs over roasting meats, or make a crispy, herb-flavoured coating.

PATES: Add chopped herbs to the mixture before cooking.

STUFFINGS: Mix chopped herbs with breadcrumbs when making stuffings.

PASTA: Add herb sprigs to the cooking water and remove before serving. Toss cooked pasta in oil or butter flavoured with garlic and chopped herbs. Use herbs in pasta sauces.

RICE: Fork chopped herbs into cooked rice.

VEGETABLE DISHES: Sprinkle chopped herbs over roasting vegetables. Add herb sprigs or a bouquet garni to the water for boiling vegetables. Put chopped herbs in vegetable casseroles. Garnish cooked vegetables with chopped herbs.

SALADS: Add chopped herbs to salad dressings. Garnish salads with whole leaves or sprigs.

SWEET DISHES: Add sprigs to stewing fruit as it cooks. Flavour sugar syrups and milk for puddings with sprigs. Garnish sweet dishes with whole leaves and sprigs.

HERB GARNISHES

The appearance of many dishes can instantly be enhanced with the addition of chopped herbs, herb sprigs or herb leaves. The garnish can be wholly or partly eaten with the dish and thereby improves the overall flavour.

Chopped fresh herbs make an attractive contrast in colour when sprinkled over a variety of cooked dishes, including casseroles, stews and braised dishes, grilled or sautéed dishes, soups; pasta and rice, and vegetable dishes.

Whole leaves, such as those of parsley, chervil, coriander, basil and mint, can be arranged singly or in patterns, either on the food or on the plate, when serving pâtés, fish cutlets and fillets, meat grills, first courses cooked in individual dishes, and sorbets and ices.

Larger herb leaves can also be used as a base for individual portions. Place a scoop of ice cream on a bed of lemon balm leaves, for example, or use a bed of rocket leaves for a small dish of prawns.

The most attractive herb sprigs are fennel, dill, tarragon, parsley and chervil. These are mostly used for decoration only and are best for dishes that are taken to the table before being served, such as whole poached fish or a joint of roast chicken.

CHOOSING THE RIGHT HERBS

There is a herb for every ingredient. These are some of the most popular combinations.

BEEF: parsley, thyme, bay, winter savory.

LAMB: thyme, lemon thyme, mint, marjoram, oregano, rosemary, tarragon, sorrel, bay.

PORK: sage, rosemary, fennel, lovage.

CHICKEN/TURKEY: parsley, thyme, lemon thyme, lemon balm, marjoram, tarragon, fennel, bay, coriander, chives, sorrel.

DUCK: sage, mint, marjoram, thyme, parsley.

GOOSE: sage, parsley, marjoram, thyme.

GAME: parsley, marjoram, thyme, winter savory, tarragon.

WHITE FISH: parsley, fennel, dill, tarragon, coriander, chives, basil, lemon thyme, lemon balm, lemon verbena.

OILY FISH: dill, fennel, chives, mint, lemon balm, sorrel, thyme, lemon thyme.

Cheese dishes: parsley, thyme, sage, mint, sorrel.

EGGS: parsley, chervil, tarragon, chives, fennel.

PULSES: parsley, marjoram, thyme, fennel, coriander, chives, basil, bay.

Herbs are so full of sunshine and sweetness that it seems there can be no tonic like them, and it is curious how appreciative invalids are of sweet scented herbs. Flower scents are often too heavy for them, but a bunch of fragrant herbs seems a perpetual joy.

ELEANOR SINCLAIR RHODE, *A GARDEN OF HERBS*, 1920s

To Stuff a Chine of Pork

Make a stuffing of the fat Leaf of Pork, Parsley, Thyme, Sage, Eggs and Crumbs of Bread, season it with Pepper, Salt, Shalot, and Nutmeg, and stuff it thick; then roast it gently.

HANNAH GLASSE, 1747

VEGETABLE DISHES: parsley, chervil, marjoram, oregano, thyme, lemon thyme, lemon balm, basil, lovage, dill.

SALADS: parsley, chervil, chives, coriander, basil, rocket, fennel, dill, lemon balm, dandelion leaves.

PASTA: basil, parsley, oregano, thyme, rosemary, marjoram.

RICE: parsley, coriander, mint.

SWEET DISHES: mint, peppermint, sweet cicely, angelica, lemon balm, lemon thyme, scented geranium, lavender.

FRESH OR DRIED

There is nothing to beat the flavour of fresh herbs but, especially if you grow your own, there will be certain times of the year when no fresh herbs are available. There are certain recipes, such as those for salads, in which dried herbs are not suitable. However, dried herbs can be substituted for fresh in dishes that require slow cooking, such as soups or casseroles. Generally speaking, because the flavour of dried herbs is very concentrated, about one-third the amount of dried herbs is equivalent to the amount of fresh herbs stipulated in a recipe.

37

CHAPTER ONE

STARTERS AND SNACKS

ttractive as garnishes and exciting as flavourings, herbs are the perfect ingredient for small, interesting dishes to start a meal. Fresh or dried, in hot or in cold dishes, they wake up your taste buds and stimulate your appetite.

STARTERS AND SNACKS

Soups, vegetables, pasta, pâtés, and light egg and meat dishes all make ideal first courses; a variety of fresh herbs lend that special touch to their flavour and appearance. Add chopped herbs to a soup just before reheating or serving, so that the two flavours blend but the herbs stay fresh. Try parsley with mushroom soup, the crisp tang of dill with creamy pumpkin, or spicy lovage with potato.

Vegetables prepared in a special way always make good starters. Fill aubergines with a rich mixture of tomatoes flavoured with fresh oregano. Use rocket as an outstanding contrast to a rich, creamy sauce for pasta, or

add tarragon to soured cream to make an unusual dip for crispy coated goujons of chicken breast.

Pâtés are always a favourite. Flavour prawn pâté with coriander, or make an unusual light pâté of curd cheese and flageolet beans seasoned with mint. Instead of serving plain toast as an accompaniment, try crispy, golden, herbed breadsticks.

Eggs make tasty starters and snacks. Use them for a mushroom and herb quiche, or for tiny omelettes to serve with marinated olives. For a really substantial snack, cook herbed pancakes filled with goat's cheese.

*A wealthy family's kitchen in the middle ages, as illustrated in an Italian breviary
(a book of psalms, hymns and prayers), 15th-century manuscript.*

41

Summer Savory *and* Caramelised Onion Frittata *with* Marinated Olives

A frittata is a flat, unfolded omelette. It can be eaten hot or cold and is ideal for summer lunches and picnics. To take it on a picnic, simply wrap the whole frittata in foil and slice it on arrival. Summer savory is a herb that has been used since the days of the Romans.

SERVES 4

15g • ½oz butter
1tbsp olive oil
2 large red onions, thinly sliced
6 eggs, beaten
2 to 3tbsp roughly chopped summer savory
Salt and freshly ground black pepper

MARINATED OLIVES
250g • 8oz mixed, unpitted black and green olives
1tbsp finely chopped fresh oregano
3tbsp olive oil
2tsp crushed coriander seeds
1tbsp lemon juice
1 small red chilli, thinly sliced and de-seeded

First marinate the olives. Place all the ingredients in a jar with a tightly fitting lid and shake well. Leave to marinate for several hours or, if possible, overnight in the refrigerator. Remove from the refrigerator at least 30 minutes before serving to allow the olives to reach room temperature.

Heat the butter and oil in a frying-pan and add the onions. Cook over a very gentle heat for 30–40 minutes, until the onions have turned golden and caramelised. Spread them out over the base of the pan and increase the heat to medium. Season the eggs and stir in the summer savory. Pour the eggs into the pan, over the onions. Stir a couple of times, to incorporate the onions, and then cook over a medium heat for about 5 minutes, until the edges begin to set. Preheat the grill to medium-high.

Once the bottom of the frittata has begun to set, put the pan under a hot grill. Grill until the frittata is set and lightly browned on top.

To serve, slice into wedges or cubes, and serve accompanied by a green salad with fresh herb salad dressing (page 121) and the marinated olives.

Goujons of Chicken *with a* Soured Cream *and* Herb Dip

Serve these tasty goujons as a starter, a light snack or as part of a buffet. The soured-cream dipping sauce uses tarragon, which goes particularly well with chicken.

SERVES 4

Oil for deep-frying
4 large skinless, boneless chicken breasts
3tbsp finely chopped fresh mixed herbs
150g • 5oz fresh white breadcrumbs, seasoned
45g • 1½oz plain flour, seasoned
3 eggs, beaten

DIPPING SAUCE
150ml • ¼ pint fresh soured cream
2tbsp finely chopped fresh tarragon
1 small garlic clove, crushed
1tbsp lemon juice
1tbsp wholegrain mustard
Pinch of salt and ground white pepper

First make the dipping sauce. Combine all the ingredients in a small bowl and set aside whilst you make the chicken, to allow the flavours to develop.

Heat the oil in a deep-fryer or large saucepan to 180°C/375°F, or until a cube of day-old bread browns in 30 seconds.

Cut the chicken into thin strips, about 10 × 2cm/4 × ¾in. Combine the mixed herbs with the breadcrumbs. Then put the flour and breadcrumbs on two separate plates and put the beaten eggs in a shallow dish. Dip the pieces of chicken first into the flour, then into the egg and finally into the breadcrumbs. Once the oil is hot enough, fry the chicken a few pieces at a time for 3–4 minutes, until crisp and golden. Drain on kitchen paper and keep warm while you cook the rest of the chicken.

Serve with the soured cream and herb dipping sauce.

43

POTATO *and* LOVAGE SOUP

Lovage is particularly suited to cooking with root vege-tables, potatoes in particular. It has a celery-like flavour and if you are unable to find it, celery is a good substitute.

SERVES 4

2tbsp olive oil	*Salt and freshly ground black*
1 medium onion, chopped	*pepper*
500g • 1lb potatoes, peeled and cubed	*Crusty bread or croûtons, to serve*
150–300ml • ¼–½ pint milk	
2–3tbsp finely chopped fresh lovage or 2 sticks of fresh finely chopped celery	TO GARNISH
	Lovage or celery leaves

Heat the oil in a large saucepan and add the onion and potatoes. If using celery instead of lovage, add the chopped celery to the onion and potatoes. Cook over a gentle heat for 10 minutes. Then pour in 750ml/1¼ pints of water and simmer gently, until the potatoes are tender. Remove from the heat and allow to cool slightly. Purée in a food processor. Return to a clean pan, season and stir in the lovage and enough milk to make a desirable consistency. Heat through, scatter lovage or celery leaves over the soup, and serve immediately, accompanied by crusty bread or croûtons.

PRAWN *and* CORIANDER PÂTÉ

If you're looking for an elegant starter that you can prepare in advance, this recipe is the answer. Prepare it in the morning and leave it to chill until just before you serve it. Coriander has a very distinctive flavour but it doesn't over-whelm the more subtle flavour of the prawns in this dish.

SERVES 4

90g • 3oz butter	*1tbsp lemon juice (optional)*
1 garlic clove, crushed	*Salt and freshly ground black*
3 spring onions, sliced	*pepper*
750g • 1½ lb raw prawns in their shells, defrosted if frozen, peeled	
	TO GARNISH
4tbsp roughly chopped fresh coriander leaves	*1tbsp roughly chopped fresh coriander leaves*
3tbsp double cream	

Melt the butter in a pan and very gently sauté the garlic and spring onions for 2 minutes, without browning the garlic. Remove the pan from the heat, add the prawns and stir to coat the prawns in the butter mixture. Transfer to a food processor and add the coriander leaves; use the pulse button to process for about 10 seconds, so that the mixture remains coarsely textured. Add the cream, lemon juice (if using) and seasoning and pulse a couple more times. Spoon the pâté into individual serving dishes and chill for a couple of hours. Alternatively, line four ramekins with cling film and fill them with pâté. Chill until you want to serve and then turn out onto serving plates.

To serve, sprinkle the chopped coriander over each pâté and offer Melba toast.

Pedanius Dioscorides, 1st century

Born of Greek origin in the 1st century AD, *Dioscorides became a Roman army surgeon, travelling with Nero's armies. Realising that there was no book recording all the contemporary information on plants and other drugs, he set about compiling one, and produced in Greek* Peri hulas Iatrikes, *or "About medicinal trees." It was translated into Latin as* De materia medica *or "About Medical Materials."*
The work illustrated and described the many medicinal plants that Dioscorides and his colleagues had discovered on their travels. It outlined their medicinal qualities and gave advice and warnings about their

application. Although there was some information about animal and mineral-based drugs, it was the section on plants that made Dioscorides famous.

MUSHROOM SOUP *with* PARSLEY

This is a soup that is versatile enough to be served at an elegant dinner party but which would not be out of place at a simple family supper. Add the garnish of wild mushrooms for a dinner party and sprinkle with chopped fresh parsley.

SERVES 4

15g • ½oz dried porcini
  (ceps)
60g • 2oz butter
4 shallots, chopped
1 garlic clove, crushed
300g • 10oz large flat-cap
  mushrooms, thickly sliced
150ml • ¼ pint dry white wine
450ml • ¾ pint chicken or
  vegetable stock
3tbsp finely chopped fresh
  parsley
3 to 5tbsp single cream

Salt and freshly ground black
  pepper

TO GARNISH
60g • 2oz mixed wild
  mushrooms (such as
  chanterelles, ceps), wiped
  and torn into bite-sized
  pieces (optional)
1tbsp chopped fresh parsley

TO SERVE
Crusty bread

Soak the dried porcini in 300ml/½ pint of hot water for 20 minutes, then strain, reserving the liquid. Strain the liquid once more through a muslin-lined sieve and chop the soaked mushrooms.

Over a medium heat, melt 45g/1½oz of the butter in a large saucepan and gently sauté the shallots for 5 minutes. Stir in the garlic and sauté for a further 2 minutes. Add the sliced mushrooms and cook gently, with the lid on, for about 5 minutes. Pour in the wine and bring to the boil; boil rapidly for 2 minutes, to reduce the wine. Pour in the stock and mushroom-soaking liquid; add the soaked mushrooms and seasoning and simmer for about 15 minutes, until the mushrooms are soft.

Remove from the heat and allow to cool slightly. Purée in a food processor, until smooth.

Return to a clean pan, stir in the parsley and cream and check the seasoning. Gently reheat.

Meanwhile, if you are making the wild-mushroom garnish, melt the remaining butter in a pan and add the wild mushrooms. Cook gently for about 5 minutes, until softened.

To serve, pour the mushroom soup into warmed, individual soup bowls and garnish with a few wild mushrooms and a sprinkling of parsley. Serve immediately with crusty bread.

45

GRAPE *and* CUCUMBER COOLER

Borage has the refreshing taste of cucumber and conjures up memories of old-fashioned summer garden parties. It is frequently used to garnish summer drinks, in particular the quintessentially British Pimms.

MAKES ABOUT 1 LITRE · 1¾ PINTS

1½ lemons
3–4 tbsp caster sugar
300ml · ½ pint orange juice, chilled
300ml · ½ pint red grape juice, chilled
475ml · 16fl oz sparkling water, chilled

Ice cubes

TO GARNISH
Cucumber slices
½ lemon
Fresh borage sprigs

Squeeze the juice from one and a half lemons and slice the remaining half-lemon into thin slices. In a jug or large bowl, combine the sugar with the orange, lemon and grape juices and stir until the sugar dissolves. Add the water and mix well. Add the ice cubes and garnish with slices of cucumber and lemon, and sprigs of borage.

MINT JULEP

This is a traditional drink from the southern United States. It is re-freshing served on a hot day and is meant to be sipped slowly.

SERVES 1

10 sprigs of mint, leaves only
1tsp sugar

2tbsp water
4tbsp brandy, whisky or bourbon
Crushed ice

Crush half the mint with the sugar and water in a small jug and mix to extract the mint flavour. Fill a glass with the crushed ice and strain over the mint mixture (discarding the mint leaves). Pour in the chosen spirit and stir gently to mix the drink. Garnish with the remaining sprigs of mint.

NON-ALCOHOLIC SUMMER PUNCH

On a balmy summer's day, often there is nothing better than a refreshing drink with a hint of fresh herbs. This punch is ideal as it is non-alcoholic, so it leaves your head clear to concentrate on other more pressing matters, such as gardening or sunbathing!

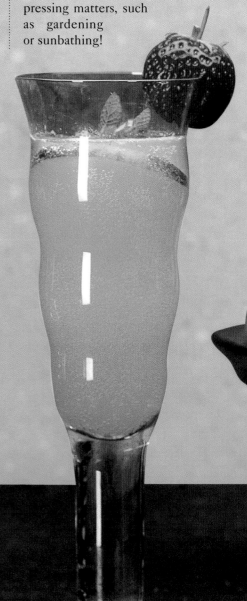

MAKES ABOUT 2½ LITRES · 4 PINTS

600ml · 1 pint	*Ice cubes*
orange juice,	*1 peach, halved*
chilled	*and sliced*
600ml · 1 pint	*12 strawberries,*
tropical fruit	*hulled and*
juice, chilled	*quartered*
1.2 litres · 2 pints	*Fresh lemon balm*
lemonade,	*and mint sprigs,*
chilled	*to garnish*

Mix the orange juice and tropical fruit juices with the lemonade in a jug or punch bowl. Add the ice cubes and fruit, and garnish with the sprigs of lemon balm and mint. Serve at once.

HERB TEA

Many fresh and dried herbs can be made into refreshing teas, including camo-mile, mint, thyme, rosemary, savory and borage.

SERVES 1

2tbsp chopped fresh	TO SERVE
herb (such as	*Lemon slices*
mint) or 1tbsp	*Sugar*
dried herb	
250ml · 8fl oz	
boiling water	

Steep your chosen fresh or dried herb in the boiling water for 4–5 minutes. Strain and serve with slices of lemon and sugar, to taste.

ALCOHOLIC SUMMER PUNCH

If you are catering for large numbers, it is often much easier to prepare a big bowl of punch, rather than serve a wide range of individual drinks. If you need a very large quantity, make it all up beforehand and store in containers until you are ready to decant it into a punch bowl or glass jug.

MAKES ABOUT 2½ LITRES · 4 PINTS

900ml · 1½ pints	*1 lime, sliced*
tropical fruit	*1 orange, sliced*
juice, chilled	*Fresh mint sprigs*
8tbsp brandy	*Fresh borage sprigs*
2 bottles sparkling	*Ice cubes*
dry white wine,	
chilled	

Mix together the fruit juice, brandy and white wine and add one or two slices of the lime and orange and a sprig or two of mint and borage. Chill in the refrigerator for at least 1 hour.

Just before serving, remove the herbs and add the remaining slices of fruit and sprigs of mint and borage. Add a few ice cubes to keep the punch cool and serve.

PUMPKIN *and* DILL SOUP

Pumpkin is a delightful vegetable that is under-used in cooking, but is, of course, a common sight in shops around Hallowe'en. Dill is particularly suited to soups made with root and winter vegetables; add it towards the end of cooking, to retain maximum flavour.

SERVES 4

30g • 1oz butter
2tbsp olive or vegetable oil
1 onion, roughly chopped
750g • 1½lb pumpkin, peeled, de-seeded and chopped
250ml • 8fl oz milk
1 to 2tbsp roughly chopped fresh dill

Salt and freshly ground black pepper

CROÛTONS
3 slices of white bread, crusts removed, cut into 1cm • ½in cubes

Preheat the oven to 220°C/425°F/gas mark 7. Melt the butter and oil in a large saucepan and add the onion and pumpkin. Cook gently for about 10 minutes. Pour in 450ml/¾ pint of hot water. Simmer gently, for about 15–20 minutes, until the pumpkin is very tender.

Meanwhile, to make the croûtons, put the cubes of bread in a bowl and pour over the oil. Season with salt and pepper and toss well. Spread the bread out on a baking sheet and bake in the oven for 5–10 minutes, until crisp.

When the soup is cooked, allow it to cool slightly. Push it through a sieve, or purée in a food processor. Return to a clean saucepan and stir in the milk. Bring to the boil, then stir in the dill and seasoning.

Serve with the croûtons or with crusty bread.

Equipment for Chopping Herbs

No special equipment is needed for chopping herbs. A large, heavy kitchen knife with a sharp, triangular-shaped blade, of the kind that you would use for chopping vegetables, is perfectly adequate when combined with a sturdy chopping board.

However, specially made herb-chopping knives are available should you prefer. One of the most popular is a curved knife with a handle at each end, sometimes called a herb-chopper or mezzaluna. These come single-bladed (usually 20 cm/8 in long) or double-bladed (about 15 cm/6 in long) with two parallel blades attached together to the handles. To use a mezzaluna on a chopping board, rock it from side to side over the herbs. Some are supplied with a bowl, into which they fit neatly. Put the herbs into the bowl and press the mezzaluna down on them repeatedly to chop them.

Also available is a herb mill, consisting of a small cylindrical container, which is filled with herbs, and a grinder. The herbs are minced by turning a handle.

PASTA *with* ROCKET *and* DOLCELATTE

Rocket is making a spectacular revival in British and American cooking, which is most welcome because this dandelion-shaped herb is absolutely delicious served in salads, tossed into pasta and even thrown fresh on to pizzas!

SERVES 4

300g • 10oz rigatoni
2tbsp olive oil
1 small onion, finely chopped
1 fat garlic clove, quartered
150ml • ¼ pint dry white wine
125g • 4oz dolcelatte cheese, cubed

250ml • 8fl oz double cream
90g • 3oz rocket leaves, long stalks removed
Salt and freshly ground black pepper

Cook the pasta in a large pan of boiling water for 10–12 minutes, until tender. Drain and keep warm.

Over a medium heat, heat the oil in a large pan, add the onion and fry gently for 8 minutes, until the onion is soft. Stir in the garlic and fry for 2 minutes more. Add the wine, increase the heat and simmer for about 4 minutes, until the wine has reduced to a syrupy consistency. Reduce the heat to medium, then stir in the cubes of dolcelatte and the cream. Stir gently, to allow the dolcelatte to melt slightly. Season with salt and freshly ground black pepper; add the cooked pasta and mix well, coating the pasta with the sauce. Stir in half the rocket and transfer to a warmed serving dish. Scatter over the remaining rocket and serve immediately.

HERB *and* MUSHROOM QUICHE

Often passed over for more fashionable foods, a well-flavoured quiche can be absolutely delicious. Here, a variety of herbs have been suggested but, if some aren't available, use what can be found. This is an ideal dish for taking on picnics or for serving at summer parties. Serve hot or at room temperature, accompanied by salad.

SERVES 4–6

350g • 12oz shortcrust pastry	*4tbsp finely chopped fresh herbs*
30g • 1oz butter	*(such as basil, parsley,*
150g • 5oz flat-cap	*chives and oregano)*
mushrooms, roughly chopped	*1tbsp finely chopped fresh thyme*
3 eggs	*leaves*
150ml • ¼ pint milk	*Salt and freshly ground black*
	pepper

This quiche can be made in either a 20 × 3cm/8 × 1¾in round tin or a 22 × 2.5cm/9 × 1in round tin. Depending on the size of the tin, roll out the pastry to a circle 8cm/3in wider than the tin and line the tin. Trim the edges, prick the base all over with a fork and chill in the refrigerator for at least 30 minutes, while you prepare the filling.

Preheat the oven to 190°C/375°F/gas mark 5. To make the filling, melt the butter in a pan and add the chopped mushrooms. Cook, uncovered, for about 5 minutes, until the mushrooms have released their juices and the juices have all but evaporated. Set aside.

Beat the eggs with the milk and stir in the chopped herbs (reserving the thyme) and seasoning.

Put the tin on a baking sheet, to make it easier to transfer the quiche in and out of the oven. Line the tin with greaseproof paper and fill it with baking beans or dried beans. Bake blind in the oven for 10 minutes. Remove the beans and greaseproof paper and pour half the filling into the pastry case; then scatter over the mushrooms. Pour over the remaining filling, sprinkle over the chopped thyme and bake in the oven for 35–40 minutes, until the filling is set and the top is golden brown.

Nicholas Culpeper, 1616–54

Nicholas Culpeper provided us with one of the most read herbals of all time – the result of a tragic love affair which caused his life to change direction.

The son of a Surrey rector, Nicholas Culpeper studied for several years at Cambridge University until he fell in love. The couple decided to elope, so he borrowed £200 from his mother (a substantial sum in those days) and arranged to meet his partner near Lewes in Sussex, where they intended to be wed. On the way, she was struck by lightning and killed.

Culpeper was too traumatised to settle to the grandeur of Cambridge society or the formalities of his education, so his grandfather paid a London apothecary £50 to employ Nicholas as an apprentice.

After some years he set up his own practice in the Spitalfields area of London, then a run-down district which was home to the poorest of the poor. Unlike conventional doctors, who would not dispense their expensive chemical potions without payment, Culpeper made himself the poor people's doctor, treating them from his own clinic with local herbs and very often waiving the fee.

His dislike of established medical practice gained him many enemies in the profession, but this did not prevent him from publishing a herbal which he entitled The English Physician. *In it he described numerous readily available and easily grown herbs, together with the remedies that they could provide. It became indispensable for housewives, who were responsible for their families' health, and is still one of the most popular herbals.*

51

SWEET MARJORAM PANCAKES

Pancakes are great favourites and filled pancakes make a substantial starter or snack. Serve on their own or with a few dressed salad leaves.

SERVES 4

125g • 4oz plain flour	FILLING
Pinch of salt	*200g • 7oz soft goat's cheese,*
1 egg	*beaten until soft*
300ml • ½ pint milk	*3 to 4tbsp milk*
1tbsp melted butter	*2 firm ripe tomatoes, blanched,*
3tbsp finely chopped fresh sweet	*peeled, de-seeded and*
marjoram	*chopped*
Butter for frying	*8 to 10 fresh basil leaves, torn*
	Salt and freshly ground black
	pepper
	60g • 2oz pitted black olives,
	roughly chopped

To make the pancakes, put the flour and salt in a bowl and make a well in the centre. Add the egg and, using an electric mixer on low speed, start to incorporate the flour into the egg. Gradually pour in the milk and whisk until a smooth batter forms. Stir in the melted butter and strain the batter through a sieve into a jug. Stir in the chopped marjoram. Cover and chill for 1 hour.

Preheat the oven to 180°C/375°F/gas mark 4. Meanwhile, make the filling. Soften the cheese to a spreadable consistency by adding a little of the milk and beating well. Add as much milk as is necessary and then mix the cheese with the remaining filling ingredients.

Put a medium-size crêpe or frying-pan (about 18cm/7in across the base) over a high heat. When the pan is very hot, melt a small knob of butter in the pan and swirl it around. Reduce the heat to medium and pour or ladle in about 2 tablespoons of batter, swirling it around to cover the base of the pan. Cook for 1–1½ minutes or less if the pancakes seem to be cooking more quickly. When the edges are brown, use a spatula to loosen the edges of the pancake. Flip it over and cook the other side for a further minute. Remove the pancake to a warmed plate and continue until all the batter is used up or you have eight good pancakes.

Divide the filling mixture between eight of the pancakes (freeze any remaining ones) and carefully spread it out to cover the base of the pancake, leaving a 2.5cm/1in border around the edge. Roll up the pancakes and put them in a single layer in a greased ovenproof dish. Warm in the pre-heated oven for 10 minutes. Serve immediately.

BAKED AUBERGINES *with* BASIL *and* OREGANO

Aubergines are eaten by many nations and are found in abundance in Mediterranean, Asian and Middle-Eastern cooking. This is a rich, exotic dish, good for hot, summery days in the garden and for cold winter-evening dinner parties, as they can be served either hot or cold.

SERVES 4

2 medium-size aubergines	*150g • 5oz mozzarella cheese,*
4tbsp olive oil	*thinly sliced*
2 garlic cloves, crushed	*45g • 1½oz fresh Parmesan*
1 onion, finely chopped	*cheese, grated*
400g • 13oz can of chopped	*Salt and freshly ground black*
tomatoes	*pepper*
2tsp sugar	*Small basil leaves, to garnish*
6 fresh basil leaves, roughly	
torn	
1tbsp finely chopped fresh	
oregano or 2tsp dried	
oregano	

Preheat the oven to 180°C/375°F/gas mark 4. Cut each aubergine in half lengthways and scoop out the flesh from each one, leaving at least a 1cm/½in edge of flesh around the edge, to prevent the aubergine from falling apart during cooking. Roughly chop half the scooped-out flesh and discard the other half.

Heat 1 tablespoon of the oil in a small saucepan and gently sauté the garlic and onion for 3–4 minutes, until the onions are soft. Add the tomatoes and aubergine flesh and bring to the boil. Stir in the sugar and seasoning and boil hard for about 5 minutes, to allow the sauce to reduce; stir frequently to prevent the sauce from burning. Remove from the heat and stir in the basil and oregano.

Divide the mixture between the aubergine shells; top with slices of mozzarella cheese and sprinkle with Parmesan cheese. Drizzle over the remaining oil. Put on a baking sheet and bake in the oven for 50–60 minutes, until the cheese has formed a delicious golden crust on the top of each aubergine.

Serve the aubergines hot or cold, garnished with small basil leaves.

52

MINTED BEAN *and* HERB PÂTÉ *with* HERBED BREAD STICKS

This is a light, fresh-tasting pâté that can be made very quickly in the food processor. The herbed bread sticks are an unusual alternative to Melba toast or crusty bread.

SERVES 4

400g • 13oz can of flageolet beans, drained and rinsed
250g • 8oz curd cheese
3tbsp natural yogurt
4tbsp roughly chopped fresh mint
1tsp chilli powder
8 slices of white bread, crusts removed

3tbsp olive oil
3tbsp finely chopped mixed fresh herbs (such as oregano, parsley, thyme, marjoram)
Salt and freshly ground black pepper
4 sprigs of fresh mint, to garnish

Preheat the oven to 180°C/375°F/gas mark 4. Put the beans, curd cheese, yogurt, mint and seasoning into a food processor and purée until fairly smooth but still with a bit of texture. Transfer to ramekins or individual serving bowls.

To make the bread sticks, cut each slice of bread into "soldiers" approximately 2cm/¾in wide. Combine the olive oil with the herbs. Toss the bread sticks in the oil and herbs, to ensure they are all evenly coated. Transfer to a baking sheet or ovenproof dish. Bake for 10 minutes, until golden. Garnish each pâté with a sprig of mint and serve with the bread sticks.

Lavender

Lavender is one of the most versatile of herbs. It has been loved for centuries for its fresh, sweet scent, its healing abilities and even its culinary properties.

A field of Norfolk lavender just before harvesting. After the fragrant flower spikes have been cut, some are dried for lavender bags and pot-pourri and the rest go through a distilling process to make lavender oil.

54

There are two main types of lavender: *Lavandula angustifolia* (also called *L. vera*, *L. officinalis* or *L. spica*), which is the one most grown commercially; and *Lavandula latifolia* (also known as spike or wild lavender).

Lavender comes from the hilly regions of the western Mediterranean and it was taken all over Europe by the Romans, for whom it was one of the most favoured plants. It is now grown commercially in France, particularly in Provence, in Italy, Norfolk in England, Norway, Australia and the United States.

Lavender is cut when the flowers are fully open and the oil content is greatest. It was once harvested by teams of women with sickles but now it is mainly gathered mechanically. Spaces of about 2 m (7 ft) are left between the rows to allow the machines to pass, and the harvester travels between the lines of lavender, lifting the stems and cutting and bagging the flower heads. Some of the lavender is dried by being laid on a ventilated floor in a drying shed and having warm air pumped around it until the flowers are crisp. The rest is put through a process of steam distillation to draw off the richly scented, golden coloured oil.

You can use dried lavender flowers with their fresh scent for pots-pourris and sweet bags and for making cosmetics, lavender bags and bath preparations.

Dried or fresh lavender is also used in the kitchen. Many dried mixtures labelled "Herbes de Provence", intended for use in omelettes and casseroles, contain a little lavender, and it

Englishwomen have forgotten, if they ever knew, that it is the scent par excellence of England, and that its aroma is more pleasing to Englishmen than any other, and more health-giving.

Mrs C.F. Leyel, *The Magic of Herbs*, 1926

Lavender Bottles

These are also called lavender wands. Hang them up in a wardrobe or place them in a drawer with your clothes. To make one bottle, cut 20 lavender sprigs with the flowers open and with long stalks. Trim the stalks to the same length and strip off any side shoots or leaves. Tie the bunch of lavender at the base of the heads and fold the stems down over the heads, spacing them evenly. Tie the stalks again at the base of the flower heads. Make another tie at the base of the stems. Cover the cotton ties with ribbon, making a loop at the stalk end for hanging. Alternatively, weave ribbon in and out of the stalks to enclose the flowers and cover the stems.

A lavender field in Provence with the plants grown in rows to make mechanical harvesting easier.

Plantations of lavender make the air smell very sweet in the summer months. Here they surround a farm in Vaucluse, France.

adds a special touch to desserts such as ice creams and fruit salads.

The healing properties of lavender and lavender oil are many. The scent is both refreshing and relaxing, and it can ease headaches and soothe the nerves. The oil is excellent for burns, chilblains and insect bites in particular.

Lavender Sugar

Sprinkle lavender sugar over fruit salads, use it to make ice creams and other desserts, add it to cake mixtures or whip it into cream-cheese frostings.

225 g • 8 oz sugar (caster or granulated)
4 lavender spikes with flowers open, stalks removed

Put the sugar into a screw-topped jar. Bruise the lavender spikes and bury them in the sugar. Cover tightly and leave for 2 weeks, shaking every day. The sugar is then ready for use. It will keep for up to one month.

Lavender Water

Put a quart of water to every pint of lavender picked from the stalk. Put them in a cold still over a slow fire. Distill very slowly, and put it into a pot till you have distilled the whole. Then clean your still well out, put your lavender water into it, and distill it off as slowly as before. Then put it into bottles, cork them quite close, and set them by for use.

FROM THE RECEIPT BOOK OF SUSANNAH STACEY,
QUOTED IN MARCUS WOODWARD,
THE MISTRESS OF STANTON'S FARM, 1938

CHAPTER TWO

VEGETABLES
AND
SALADS

dd chopped fresh herbs to a
simply cooked vegetable to
transform its appearance and flavour.
Whether you are boiling, steaming or
stir-frying vegetables, producing purées or
summer salads, a sprinkling of herbs
will make every vegetable dish special.

VEGETABLES AND SALADS

All vegetables, whether raw or cooked, can benefit from the addition of chopped fresh herbs. For cooked vegetables, the easiest approach is to toss them in herbs and melted butter. Try lemon thyme and fennel with spring greens; or use crème fraîche in place of butter, and add it with chervil to baby carrots. Another way to include herbs after cooking is to stir them into a creamy vegetable purée. Seasoning the vegetables with herbs during cooking also produces an excellent range of flavours. Simmer peas and lettuce with parsley and chervil, or cannelloni and pinto beans with thyme and marjoram.

The most flavoursome salads can be created with a mixture of unusual herbs, freshly picked from the garden. Try a combination of avocado and wild mushrooms, mixed in a basil and lemon dressing and spooned over peppery-flavoured rocket leaves and crispy croûtons. Use bulgur wheat with parsley and mint to make an authentic Middle Eastern tabbouleh; or reproduce the flavour of Greece with tomatoes, onion, olives, feta cheese and oregano.

Majoram harvesting, Tacuinum Sanitatum *manuscript, c. 1385.*

59

PEAS *with* LETTUCE, PARSLEY *and* CHERVIL

This is a typically French way of serving peas. Parsley and chervil are both very aromatic herbs and make this dish a light accompaniment, suited to most meat and fish dishes.

SERVES 4

250g • 8oz shelled peas
1 small lettuce or 180g • 6oz
   lettuce leaves, shredded
4 spring onions, chopped
2tbsp chopped fresh parsley
2tbsp chopped fresh chervil
1tsp salt
1tsp sugar
30g • 1oz butter

Put all the ingredients in a saucepan, add 3 tablespoons of water and mix well. Bring to the boil and then turn down the heat and leave to simmer, covered, for 15 minutes. There should be very little liquid left in the pan at the end of cooking. Serve the peas with any juices that are left.

60

Companion Planting

Herbs can be beneficial to other plants growing near them, chiefly in keeping away insect pests by means of their strong scents. For this reason, herbs are sometimes planted in the vegetable garden or amongst flowers. Some aromatic plants, such as sage, marjoram, hyssop and thyme, generally improve the health of the soil and of other plants growing round them. The reason why

this happens has not been scientifically proved. Herbs to plant near carrots to deter carrot fly: garlic, chives, pennyroyal, nasturtium, sage, rosemary, southernwood. Herbs to repel whitefly: nasturtium, French marigold. Herbs to plant near cabbages: nasturtium, sage, mint. Herbs to plant near tomatoes: French marigold, basil.

HERBED FRIED COURGETTES

This dish is suitable for serving with most meat and fish recipes. The courgette slices are coated in a herb and flour mixture and then fried in butter. Using a plastic bag to coat the courgettes in the flour prevents the flour from making a mess everywhere.

SERVES 4

2tbsp plain flour	3 courgettes, weighing about
1tsp salt	430g • 14oz each, cut in
Freshly ground black pepper	1cm • ½in slices
3tbsp chopped fresh mixed	2tsp vegetable oil
herbs (such as parsley, thyme	45g • 1½oz butter
and oregano)	

Combine the flour, salt, pepper and herbs in a plastic bag. Add the courgette slices. Then, holding the bag by the opening (thus sealing the bag), shake the courgettes until they are all coated in the herby flour.

   Heat the butter and oil in a large frying-pan and, once the butter has melted, add the coated courgette slices and sauté them for 3 minutes on each side, until the courgette slices are golden brown. Remove from the pan and serve immediately.

THYME-ROASTED POTATOES

Roast potatoes are loved by nearly everyone and these thyme-flavoured ones are delicious served with roast meats and other vegetables. Try giving the same treatment to parsnips: they are equally scrumptious!

SERVES 4

750g • 1½lb potatoes	6 fresh thyme sprigs
6tbsp olive oil	

Preheat the oven to 190°C/375°F/gas mark 5. Peel the potatoes and cut them into chunks. Put the chunks into boiling, salted water, cook for 5 minutes, then drain.

   Pour the oil into a shallow roasting tin and heat it in the preheated oven, for 3–4 minutes. Carefully tip the potatoes and the thyme into the hot oil, turning the potatoes to coat them with oil. Roast in the oven for 50–60 minutes. Turn them occasionally, so they are evenly browned and flavoured with thyme.

BABY NEW CARROTS *with* CREME FRAICHE *and* CHERVIL

Tender young carrots have a delicious, sweet flavour, which combines well with the slightly aniseed flavour of chervil. This is an ideal dish for serving during the summer, when carrots are at their sweetest. If chervil is unavailable, parsley is a good alternative.

SERVES 4

375g • 12oz baby new carrots
1tsp sugar
7tbsp crème fraîche
3tbsp finely chopped chervil or flat-leaf parsley

Salt and freshly ground black pepper

To prepare the carrots, simply rinse under cold water, brushing off any soil or dirt, and then top and tail them. Peel them if preferred, although this is not essential with baby carrots. Put the carrots in a medium-size saucepan with 4 tablespoons of water and the sugar. Cover the pan with foil and then the lid and leave to simmer very gently for 5 minutes, or until the carrots are tender.

Remove from the heat and drain off any excess water. Return the carrots to a very gentle heat and stir in the crème fraîche, chervil or parsley and seasoning. Cook for 2 minutes, until the crème fraîche has melted and is heated through. Transfer to a warmed serving dish and serve immediately.

TABBOULEH *with* PARSLEY *and* MINT

This is a very popular dish in the Middle East. Masses of parsley, mint and lemon juice give it a very refreshing taste and a real zing. Serve it as part of a selection of starters, on its own as a salad or with pitta bread as a light lunch.

SERVES 4

125g • 4oz bulgar wheat
  (cracked wheat)
1 red onion, finely chopped
250g • 8oz tomatoes, de-seeded
  and diced
120ml • 4fl oz olive oil

50ml • 2fl oz lemon juice
5tbsp finely chopped fresh flat-
  leaf parsley
2tbsp finely chopped fresh mint
Salt and freshly ground black
  pepper

Rinse the bulgar wheat under cold running water, then place in a large saucepan and cover with 600ml/1 pint of water. Bring to the boil, cover and simmer for 10–15 minutes, until the wheat is tender and the water has been absorbed. Drain the wheat well then fluff with a fork to separate the grains.

Stir in the onion, tomatoes, olive oil, lemon juice, herbs and seasoning, mix well and allow to cool to room temperature. This dish can be prepared up to one day in advance. Simply combine all the ingredients, cover and chill in the fridge.

Herb Recipes from Around the World

Many countries are renowned for certain recipes. Try making American country-style chicken pie, Mexican salsa or Russian lobio for authentic flavours from all around the world.

Sage is one of the most popular culinary herbs in Britain.

Dill pickles are frequently made in Eastern Europe and the herb is essential in the preparation of Gravad Lax, marinated salmon from Scandinavia.

USA
COUNTRY-STYLE CHICKEN PIE
A pie made from chicken poached with vegetables and six parsley sprigs for flavour, cooled, boned and the meat left in large pieces. It is placed in a dish lined with rich pastry, coated in sauce made from the poaching stock and cream, then the chicken pieces are covered with more pastry and baked.

CANADA
STUFFED BREAM BAKED IN RED WINE
Bream stuffed with a mixture of breadcrumbs, parsley, sweet red pepper, egg yolk and lemon juice, put into a dish with a mixture of red wine and crushed garlic and baked.

MEXICO
SALSA MEXICANA
A sauce to serve with tortillas made by combining peeled, chopped tomatoes, a chopped chilli pepper, chopped onion, salt and chopped cilantro leaves. Cilantro is a herb similar to coriander, which is used in Mexico, China and Southeast Asia.

GREAT BRITAIN
SAGE AND ONION STUFFING
A mixture of onions softened in butter, breadcrumbs, salt, pepper and sage, moistened with stock, milk or cider. It is used for pork and poultry, particularly goose.

SCANDINAVIA
GRAVAD LAX
Fresh salmon, marinated for at least 48 hours with dill, salt, sugar and crushed peppercorns. It is served raw with lemon wedges and mustard sauce.

GERMANY
RINDFLEISCH MIT SCHNITTLAUCHSOSSE (BOILED BEEF WITH CHIVE SAUCE)
A joint of beef boiled with vegetables and parsley sprigs, served with a sauce made from the thickened cooking liquid flavoured with chopped chives and freshly grated nutmeg.

Nutmeg is classed as a spice rather than a herb. In its dried form it is often added to savoury dishes with fresh herbs.

FRANCE
POULET À L'ÉSTRAGON (CHICKEN WITH TARRAGON)
A chicken stuffed with several tablespoons of butter beaten with tarragon, garlic, salt and pepper, and with tarragon sprigs laid over the breast. It is roasted, basted with olive oil, then flamed in brandy. The juices are enriched with cream.

SPAIN
HABAS A LA CATALANA (BROAD BEANS WITH SAVOURY SAUSAGE AND MINT)
Broad beans cooked with diced chorizo sausage and salt pork, spring onions, a bay leaf and chopped mint.

ITALY

PESTO

A sauce for pasta which is made by pounding together fresh basil leaves, pine nuts and garlic, and mixing the paste with Parmesan and Pecorino cheeses and either olive oil or a little softened butter.

GREECE

ARNI PSITO (ROAST LAMB)

A leg or shoulder of lamb prepared by having slits cut into the skin and rosemary leaves and slivers of garlic pushed into them. It is put into a roasting tin and surrounded by sliced potatoes. Olive oil, water and lemon juice are poured over the potatoes, which are then topped with a generous sprinkling of chopped oregano. They are roasted together until the meat is tender, the water absorbed and the potatoes browned.

EASTERN EUROPE

DILL CUCUMBERS

Small cucumbers pickled in white vinegar with sprigs of dill and dill seeds to give them a distinctive flavour.

RUSSIAN FEDERATION

LOBIO

A dish of red kidney beans from the Caucasus. The cooked beans are mixed with a dressing of oil, white-wine vinegar, finely chopped onion and a blend of chopped parsley and coriander, and served cold as a salad.

SOUTH AFRICA

JUGGED VENISON

A recipe made from diced venison stewed with onions, celery and lemon juice, and flavoured with a bouquet garni of bay leaves, parsley, peppercorns and cloves.

MIDDLE EAST

TZVAZEGH

These are small omelettes flavoured with mint and parsley, and served either as a first course or as a snack in warm pitta breads. They are traditionally eaten at Easter.

INDIA

CORIANDER AND MINT CHUTNEY

A hot, green relish made by liquidising fresh coriander and mint with green chilli, fresh root ginger and lemon juice.

CHINA

STIR-FRIED DISHES

The most used herb in Chinese cooking is garlic. For many stir-fried dishes it is crushed and sautéed in peanut oil with grated fresh ginger and chopped spring onions before the main ingredients are added.

SOUTHEAST ASIA

GULAI TUMIS (SOUR FISH CURRY)

In this dish from Malaysia dried chillies, lemon grass, browned onions, garlic and spices are minced together to a fine paste and then sautéed in oil. French beans and tamarind water are added, and then fish cutlets.

It is always useful to have your own dried herbs hanging up in the kitchen. Here are bay, rosemary, sage and thyme.

65

For a good, year-round supply of fresh herbs it is a good idea to grow your own. If you do not have a large space in the garden, they can be grown successfully in pots.

66

AVOCADO, WILD MUSHROOM *and* ROCKET SALAD *with* ITALIAN DRESSING

This is an adventurous salad, perfect as a dinner-party starter. Peppery rocket leaves are combined with the delicate flavours of wild mushrooms, then tossed in an Italian dressing and piled onto toasted French bread. Serve this dish as soon after preparing as possible.

SERVES 4

½ French stick, about 20cm •
   8in long
1 garlic clove, halved
3tbsp olive oil
1 ripe avocado, halved, peeled
   and sliced
125g • 4oz wild mushrooms
   (such as chanterelle and
   porcini)
60g • 2oz rocket leaves

DRESSING
5tbsp extra-virgin olive oil
1tbsp balsamic vinegar
1tsp lemon juice
6 fresh basil leaves, finely torn
Salt and freshly ground black
   pepper

Preheat the grill to high. Cut the French stick into eight thin slices, on the diagonal, and rub each with garlic on both sides. Put on a baking tray and drizzle with 2 tablespoons of the oil. Place under the hot grill and grill for 2–3 minutes on both sides, until golden brown and toasted.

Meanwhile, heat the remaining tablespoon of oil in a frying-pan and gently sauté the wild mushrooms for about 5 minutes. Transfer to a plate to cool slightly.

Combine the dressing ingredients in a screw-topped jar and shake well. Put the rocket leaves in a bowl and pour over half the dressing. Toss the leaves well. Put two slices of bread on each plate, divide the rocket leaves between them and top with slices of avocado and the wild mushrooms. Pour over the remaining dressing and serve.

Alternatively put the rocket, avocado and wild mushrooms in a large bowl, pour over the dressing and toss well. Arrange the slices of French bread around the edge of the bowl and serve as soon as possible.

SHREDDED CABBAGE *and* SPRING GREENS *with* FENNEL *and* LEMON BALM

Lemon balm is a very fast-growing herb, so this recipe is a good way of making use of it. This dish makes an ideal accompaniment to Sunday roasts.

SERVES 4

Pinch of salt
375g • 12oz white cabbage,
   shredded
375g • 12oz spring greens,
   shredded
30g • 1oz butter, cubed

1tsp fennel seeds or 1tbsp finely
   chopped feathery fronds
   from fresh fennel
4tbsp roughly chopped fresh
   lemon balm
Freshly ground black pepper

Place 150ml/¼ pint of water and a pinch of salt in a large saucepan and bring to the boil. Add the cabbage and spring greens and simmer gently, with the lid on, for 8 minutes. Remove the lid and increase the heat, to evaporate off the liquid. Add the butter, fennel, lemon balm and pepper to the pan and allow the butter to melt. Toss the vegetables in the butter and herbs and transfer to a warmed serving dish. Serve immediately.

WINTER BEANS *with* THYME, MARJORAM *and* PARSLEY

There are many varieties of beans available. This recipe suggests using cannellini and pinto beans, but almost any combination could be used in this dish where the beans are simmered in a delicious tomato and mixed herb stew. Serve as an accompaniment to meat and poultry dishes or with boiled rice and crusty bread for a complete meal. Great for visiting vegetarians or just for a change at any meal.

SERVES 4

150g • 5oz canned cannellini beans

150g • 5oz canned pinto beans

2tbsp oil

1 large onion, halved and sliced

1 fat garlic clove, crushed

400g • 13oz fresh or canned tomatoes, chopped

1tbsp chopped fresh thyme leaves

2tbsp finely chopped fresh marjoram

4tbsp finely chopped fresh parsley

1tbsp soy sauce

Salt and freshly ground black pepper

Rinse the beans under cold running water and drain them well. Set aside.

Heat the oil in a large saucepan and gently fry the onion for 10 minutes, until softened. Stir in the garlic and cook for a further minute. Add the tomatoes, thyme, marjoram and 1 tablespoon of the parsley. Stir well and bring to the boil. Reduce the heat and leave to simmer gently for 10 minutes. Stir in the beans, soy sauce and seasoning and simmer for a further 5–10 minutes, until the beans are heated through. Remove from the heat and stir in the remaining parsley. Serve immediately.

HERB SALAD

Some herb leaves are more commonly associated with the garden than the kitchen. Leaves such as dandelion and nasturtium are perfectly edible (so long as they have not been contaminated with pesticides or traffic fumes, of course) and make an unusual talking point at dinner. Pick undamaged, young leaves and wash them well before using. Leaves such as dandelion are rich in vitamin A, calcium and iron, and are very nutritious.

Place all the salad leaves and sprigs of herbs in a bowl and mix them together. Combine the olive oil, balsamic vinegar and seasoning in a screw-topped jar and shake to combine them thoroughly.

Just before serving, pour the dressing over the salad leaves and toss well. Scatter the edible flowers over the top and serve immediately.

SERVES 4

60g • 2oz mixed herb leaves
   (such as dandelion,
   nasturtium and red
   mustard)
90g • 3oz rocket leaves
1 Little Gem lettuce, each leaf
   torn in three
10 sprigs fresh flat-leaved
   parsley, coriander and/or
   chervil

DRESSING
4tbsp olive oil
1tbsp balsamic vinegar
Salt and freshly ground black
   pepper

TO SERVE
Borage, nasturtium or other
   edible flowers

GREEK SALAD *with* OREGANO DRESSING

One of the best things about a holiday in Greece is the first taste of an authentic Greek salad, made with salty feta cheese, plump olives and rich olive oil, eaten with the sun beating down. Recreate a piece of Greece with the salad below, which is tossed in an oregano dressing.

SERVES 4

1 small red onion, sliced
180g • 6oz feta cheese, cubed
20 black olives
1 small green pepper, de-seeded and sliced
4 small ripe tomatoes or 1 large beef tomato, roughly chopped

DRESSING
3tbsp olive oil, preferably extra-virgin
1tbsp lemon juice
2 tbsp finely chopped fresh oregano
Freshly ground black pepper

TO SERVE (OPTIONAL)
Lettuce or salad leaves
Cucumber, cubed

Put the onion, feta cheese, olives, green pepper and tomatoes in a bowl and mix well. Put the dressing ingredients in a screw-topped jar and shake well. Pour the dressing over the salad and toss well. If you like, serve the Greek salad on a bed of salad leaves and cucumber.

CARROT *and* CORIANDER PUREE

Instead of serving boiled or roasted carrots at Sunday lunch, this quick vegetable purée makes a tasty alternative.

SERVES 4

750g • 1½lb carrots, peeled and cut in 1cm • ½in slices
4tbsp roughly chopped fresh coriander leaves

3tbsp single cream
Fresh coriander sprigs, to garnish

Put the sliced carrots in a medium-size saucepan and just cover them with water. Cover with the saucepan lid, bring to the boil and then leave to simmer for 15 minutes, or until the carrots are very tender. Drain well. Put the carrots in a food processor with the chopped coriander and cream and process to a smooth purée. Or, push the carrots through a sieve or *mouli-légumes* and stir in the chopped coriander.

Return the carrots to a clean pan and gently heat through. Serve garnished with coriander sprigs.

Galen, c. AD130–200

Galen was born in Pergamum in Asia Minor and moved to Alexandria to study at its famous medical school and later to practise medicine.

Galen became famous for treating gladiators after their skirmishes in the arena. He acquired such a distinguished reputation that on going to Rome, he was invited to become the personal physician of the emperor Marcus Aurelius. When the emperor died in AD 180, Galen kept his position and was physician to succeeding emperors until his own death.

Galen believed that all disease arose from the imbalance of the body's four humours: blood, bile, phlegm and choler. He chose all his plant remedies in relation to these, rating them on a four-point scale, saying, for example, "This plant is hot and moist in the third degree." From him came the term "simple," meaning a herb possessing a single quality, such as heat.

Not long after Galen's death, the Roman Empire collapsed, removing the likelihood of any early challenge to his views. In fact his ideas remained influential for many hundreds of years and were not completely overturned until the end of the 17th century.

American Indian Medicine

The medicine that was practised by Native Americans in the 17th century involved the use of herbs that were new to the colonists, but many were soon included in the list of standard household remedies, and are still being used today.

This etching shows the lodge of a Midiwine holy man during an initiation ceremony. The initiate, as he passed from lodge to lodge, learned more of the medicinal qualities of certain herbs.

When the first settlers left England to settle in Plymouth and Boston on the East Coast of America, the local people they encountered were fit and strong. They lived mainly outdoors, eating a diet of fresh wild meat, raw fruit and vegetables, whole grains, nuts and unpolluted spring water. Alcohol was virtually unknown to them and the smoking of tobacco had a ritual purpose rather than being a regular part of daily life. They felt at one with their surroundings and they had an intimate knowledge of the plants that they found in their immediate vicinity.

When they were ill, their cures were almost always herbal. Parasitic diseases, such as worms, were the most common, so there were many herbal emetics and purges. After the cause of the disease had been expelled, healing herbal decoctions (essences extracted by boiling) were administered while the patient

The scalp dance, as it was recorded by George Caitlin in 1844.

fasted. The fast was followed by a light, vegetarian diet until good health had been restored.

Internal remedies tended to be specific – using a single herb for a particular illness. Many were boiled as a decoction; others were steeped for a long time in cold water. Besides the leafy parts of plants the Indians also used roots and barks, which were dried and then crushed between flat stones. Oils were extracted from nuts, and ointments were made with animal fat.

American Indians enjoyed a feast on ceremonial occasions which was prepared by special cooks. Here, ingredients are being added to a large pot while, in the backgound, herbs are being ground for seasoning.

One herb that the settlers found useful was *Eupatorium perfoliatum*, which became known as boneset. All the Indian tribes used it for fevers and chills, and boneset tea became a common settlers' remedy for malaria, influenza and typhoid.

Other herbal applications were not shared between tribes, and in some cases the same herb was used for a range of different treatments. The blue flag (*Iris versicolor*), for example, was used as an emetic by the Ojibwa, as a poultice for leg ulcers by the Albany Indians, and as a decoction for colds and chest ailments by the Meskwakis.

The American Indians knew that sometimes body and mind had to be cured together, and healing rituals that involved chanting and drumming united the force of the whole tribe in treating a patient. One of the most widely practised combined treatments for mental and physical health was the ritual cleansing that took place in the sweat lodge. This was a religious experience as well as a healing process, and in some cases it served as an initiation rite. Sweat lodges took a number of forms. In the northeast, they consisted of wooden frames covered with birch bark or animal skins. In the southeast, they were earth mounds dug into a hillside beside a stream; and in the northwest, they were made of cedar planks. They were often heated by means of

hot stones, sometimes sprinkled with aromatic herbs. Within this small shelter, the patient, spiritual seeker or initiate would sweat out the impurities of body and mind.

At the beginning of the 20th century, American Indian knowledge and traditions were in danger of being stamped out and forgotten. Today, they are undergoing a revival as their values are being recognised.

The Indian shaman, or medicine man, used drumming, dance and chanting as part of his cures. Herbs were also an essential part of the healing process.

CHAPTER THREE

MEAT AND POULTRY

Take one basic meat ingredient, and you can produce a whole variety of different dishes simply by changing the herbs that you use to flavour it. And with the wide selection of meats, poultry, and herbs available, you have endless choice of style and flavour.

MEAT AND POULTRY

Certain classic dishes are always associated with particular combinations of herbs. One of these is beef en croûte, *in which a fillet of beef is encased in pastry with onions, parsley, oregano, thyme and sage. Lamb and mint are another time-honoured partnership, and a mint and yogurt sauce is particularly good with grilled lamb chops. Sage and onion stuffing is the traditional accompaniment to roast pork; but marjoram also works well either with pork cooked in cream and cider or mixed with parsley and thyme to flavour succulent home-made pork sausages. One of the most versatile meats is chicken. Pot roast it with vegetables and a bouquet garni for a farmhouse-style dinner. For a light, healthy meal, slowly bake chicken breasts in a foil parcel with fresh ginger, soy sauce, chives and tarragon; or make an authentic Thai curry, flavoured with lemon grass. For a very special meal, stuff oven-ready quail with a mixture of goat's cheese and tarragon, and grill with* herbes de Provence.

Pig killing in December, as illustrated in the Breviary of Henry 1 of Este *(a book of psalms, hymns and prayers), 15th-century manusript.*

FILLET OF BEEF EN CROUTE *with* HERBS *and* RED-WINE SAUCE

This is a delicious treat for serving at Sunday lunch or at a dinner party. Buy the thick end of the fillet for this dish, if you can. Although dried herbs can be substituted, fresh ones make all the difference.

SERVES 4

1tbsp sunflower oil	*1tbsp finely chopped fresh sage*
30g • 1oz butter	*275g • 9oz puff pastry,*
625g • 1¼lb fillet beef (thick	*defrosted if frozen*
end)	*1 small egg, beaten*
2 onions, finely chopped	*Salt and freshly ground black*
1tbsp finely chopped fresh	*pepper*
parsley	
1tbsp finely chopped fresh	SAUCE
oregano	*1tbsp plain flour*
1tbsp finely chopped fresh	*300ml • 10fl oz red wine*
thyme	*300ml • 10fl oz beef stock*

Preheat the oven to 220°C/425°F/gas mark 7. Heat the oil and butter in a frying-pan and fry the beef until it is browned all over. Remove the beef from the pan and leave it to cool. Fry the onions in the same pan, with any fat or juices left from the beef, for 10 minutes, until soft and golden. Use a slotted spoon to transfer the onions to a bowl, leaving any fat in the pan. Stir the herbs into the onions and season well.

Roll out the pastry on a lightly floured work surface, to a size large enough to encase the beef. Spoon three-quarters of the onion and herb mixture over the pastry, leaving a 4cm/2in border all around the edge. Put the beef in the centre of the pastry and spread the remaining onion mixture over the top. Enclose the beef in the pastry, sealing the edge with beaten egg and trimming off any excess pastry. Place the parcel on a greased baking sheet seal-side down. Using any trimmings, cut out leaves or make other decorations. Brush the whole parcel with more beaten egg, add any decorations and brush these with beaten egg. Make a small hole in the middle of the pastry, to allow steam to escape. Bake in the oven for 40 minutes for rare beef, 50–55 minutes for medium beef and 60–80 minutes for well done beef.

Meanwhile, make the sauce. Stir the flour into the pan juices and cook for 1 minute. Gradually add the wine and stock, stirring to remove any lumps, and bring to the boil. Season well, reduce the heat and simmer for 5 to 10 minutes, until the sauce is reduced slightly. Strain into a gravy boat.

To serve, carefully transfer the beef to a warmed serving dish, without breaking the pastry. Carve it into slices at the table, and serve accompanied by the red-wine sauce.

GRILLED QUAIL STUFFED *with* TARRAGON

Although this dish is a little fiddly to prepare, it is well worth the effort for an elegant dinner. The birds are stuffed under the skin with a delightful mixture of tarragon, goat's cheese and mushrooms. They can be prepared in advance and kept refrigerated until you cook them. Serve accompanied by sauté potatoes and green vegetables.

SERVES 4

4 oven-ready quail	Stuffing
2tsp dried herbes de	*2tbsp olive oil*
Provence – *thyme, summer*	*125g • 4oz button mushrooms,*
savory, lavender and	*very finely chopped*
rosemary (optional)	*1 fat garlic clove, crushed*
Salt and freshly ground black	*90g • 3oz soft goat's cheese*
pepper	*3 to 4tbsp finely chopped fresh*
	tarragon

First prepare the stuffing. Heat 1 tablespoon of the oil in a frying-pan and gently fry the mushrooms, uncovered, for 4–5 minutes, until most of the liquid in the pan has evaporated. Stir in the crushed garlic for the last minute. Remove the pan from the heat and allow the mushrooms to cool in the pan for about 10 minutes. Then stir in the goat's cheese, tarragon and seasoning, mix to a smooth consistency and leave to cool completely.

To prepare each quail, put the quail breast-side down and, using poultry shears, cut along both sides of the backbone, to split open the bird. Discard the backbone. Open the bird out and turn it over so it is breast-side up. Press down with the heel of your hand to break the breastbone and rib cage and flatten out the bird. From the neck end, carefully separate the breast skin from the flesh. Divide the stuffing into four and then, using your fingers, carefully push the stuffing under the skin of each bird, smoothing the surface of each bird once it is stuffed. Fold the skin over the opening, to seal. Using a small knife, make a slit in the skin between the legs and then bend and tuck the legs through the slit, to keep the bird in a neat shape.

Preheat the grill to high. Rub each bird with the remaining olive oil and sprinkle over the *herbes de Provence* (if using). Grill, breast-side down, for about 20 minutes. Turn the birds over and grill them for a further 10 minutes. Depending on how well done you want the meat, cook the quail for a slightly longer or shorter period of time.

The Physicians of Myddfai, 13th century

The physicians of Myddfai in Wales were said to have been founded by Rhiwallon, the legendary son of the magical lady from the Lake of Llyn y Van Vach and a local farmer. When the lady returned to her lake she is said to have passed the knowledge of healing herbs to Rhiwallon, who formed the order of the physicians of Myddfai with his three sons.

Members of the order served as personal physicians to the Princes of South Wales for nearly 1,000 years, ending in the 19th century when the last of the line was buried. At the beginning of the 13th century, their lord of the manor, Rys Gryg, encouraged them to record their knowledge for posterity.

The physicians used what we would now call a holistic approach to medicine, emphasising each patient's responsibility for his or her own health and treating the causes of the disease as well as the symptoms. In devising a cure the health of the patient's whole body was looked at, as well as his or her state of mind. Their writings not only give herbal cures but also philosophies of healthy living, such as: "The bread of yesterday, the meat of today, and the wine of last year will produce health."

They had at their disposal around 900 herbs, mainly those that grew prolifically in their area, both wild and cultivated in garden plots. They specified the parts to use and the amounts, as well as the need for such things as clean water for their infusions, decoctions and poultices. Theirs was a sensible, simple medicine that would not be out of place today.

LAMB *with* YOGURT *and* MINT SAUCE

Lamb is traditionally served with mint and this recipe uses mint with a refreshing yogurt sauce. This dish tastes wonderful accompanied by small new potatoes and a vegetable or two, or a salad.

SERVES 4

2 racks of lamb, each with 6–7 cutlets	SAUCE
1tbsp olive or vegetable oil	*1tbsp olive or vegetable oil*
	150g • 5oz natural yogurt
	3tbsp finely chopped fresh mint
	Pinch of salt and white pepper

First make the sauce. Combine all the ingredients together in a bowl and leave the flavours to develop while you prepare the lamb.

Preheat the oven to 190°C/375°F/gas mark 5. Take the racks of lamb and slice away any skin and excess fat, leaving a thin, even layer of fat. Score the fat with diagonal cuts in a diamond pattern and season with salt and pepper. Roast in the oven for 25–30 minutes for slightly pink meat or for 30–40 minutes for medium to well done meat.

Carve the racks of lamb into individual cutlets and serve with the yogurt and mint sauce.

DUCK BREASTS *with* ORANGE *and* MINT

Duck *à l'orange* is probably one of the most famous recipes for duck and fruit. This recipe is a variation on the theme, with the addition of mint, which goes surprisingly well with orange. Serve the duck with sauté or roast potatoes and green beans.

SERVES 4

3 oranges	*1tbsp brown sugar*
3 large duck breasts (with the skin on), such as Barbary, cut into large pieces	*4tbsp finely chopped mint leaves*
1tbsp olive oil	*Salt and freshly ground black pepper*
1tbsp plain flour	*3tbsp port*
300ml • 10fl oz good-quality duck or chicken stock	

Thinly peel the zest (not the pith) from two of the oranges and cut it into thin strips. Then remove all the pith and segment the oranges. Blanch the strips of orange zest in boiling water for 5 minutes, then drain and set them aside. Squeeze the juice from the remaining orange and set it aside.

Heat the olive oil in a large frying-pan over a high heat and fry the duck breasts until thoroughly browned on all sides. Remove the duck from the pan and keep warm. Remove all but a tablespoon of fat from the pan, sprinkle in the flour and mix to form a paste. Cook for a couple of minutes, stirring frequently to scrape up any bits left in the pan. Gradually pour in the stock, stirring to form a smooth sauce, then stir in the sugar, orange juice and zest and season with salt and pepper. Bring to the boil, reduce the heat and add the pieces of duck. Simmer for a further 5 minutes, adding the mint leaves and orange segments for the final 2 minutes. Check the seasoning and add the port. Serve immediately.

THAI CHICKEN CURRY *with* CORIANDER *and* LEMON GRASS

Thai curries have very thin sauces, compared to Indian curries, so provide plenty of boiled rice to mop up the sauce.

SERVES 4

2.5cm • 1in piece of fresh root ginger, peeled and chopped	*4 skinless, boneless chicken breasts, shredded*
3 fresh red chillies, de-seeded and roughly chopped	*400g • 13oz can of coconut milk*
2 garlic cloves, chopped	*227g • 7½oz can of bamboo shoots*
2 shallots, chopped	
5cm • 2in piece of lemon grass, finely chopped	*90g • 3oz button mushrooms, quartered*
2tsp coriander seeds	*3–4tbsp roughly chopped fresh coriander leaves*
1tsp salt	
1tbsp vegetable oil	

In a pestle and mortar (or a coffee grinder if you keep one solely for spices), grind together the ginger, chillies, garlic, shallots, lemon grass, coriander seeds and salt, to a paste. If you do not have either, put the ingredients in a small bowl and use the end of a rolling pin to crush everything.

Heat the oil over a high heat in a frying-pan or wok and fry the paste for 30 seconds. Add the shredded chicken and stir-fry for 2 minutes. Pour in the coconut milk and bring to the boil, then reduce the heat, cover the pan and leave to simmer for 10 minutes. Add the bamboo shoots and mushrooms and simmer for a further 2 minutes.

Remove the pan from the heat, stir in the coriander leaves and serve, accompanied by boiled rice.

Herbs in a Monastery Garden

Imagine peace and stillness, the humming of bees, bird song, the sound of a trickling fountain and, wafting over it, the aromatic scent of herbs. Herb gardens in monasteries all over Europe from the 9th to 15th centuries were very much like this.

A selection of different thymes that would have been grown in a monastery garden. They were useful in the kitchen and also in the infirmary where they were made into remedies for coughs and colds.

Herbs were important in monastic life. They enlivened the plain daily meals in the refectory; they provided medicines for the monks and for the local villagers; they were strewn on the floor of the abbey, giving out a sweet scent as they were crushed underfoot; and they helped to keep living and sleeping quarters free of insect pests. The herb garden itself was a place of calm and solace, where the monks could sit and contemplate beneath arbours of bay or honeysuckle.

A list of useful herbs, both medicinal and culinary, was drawn up in the 9th century by Charlemagne, King of the Franks and Emperor of the Holy Roman Empire, advised by Alcuin, an English monk who had become abbot of the monastery of St Martin at Tours in France. Soon afterwards, Walafrid Strabo, a monk at the island monastery of Reichenau in Switzerland, wrote a list of 29 plants that he considered to be the most valuable. Between them, these lists had a great influence on monastery gardens until the time of the Reformation in the 16th century.

The monastery garden was often described as the *hortus conclusus* (enclosed garden) because it was surrounded by a wattle fence about 1.2 m (4 ft) high. This was made in spring, when the young shoots of hazel and willow were supple. Stakes were driven into the ground around the garden and the shoots were woven between them. The fence kept out animals, such as deer and rabbits, and any human thieves who wanted to help themselves to the monastery's herbs and vegetables. It also gave a sense of peace and privacy.

One monk, often called the herberer, was in charge of the herb garden, and he had a team of helpers, usually sturdy young novices, to do the digging. Gardening was the same for a medieval monk as it is for a herb gardener today: in the spring there would be sowing and

Medieval monks weeding in the monastery garden.

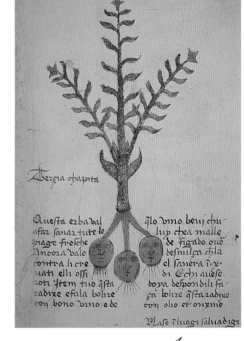

An illustration from a 14th-century Italian herbal.

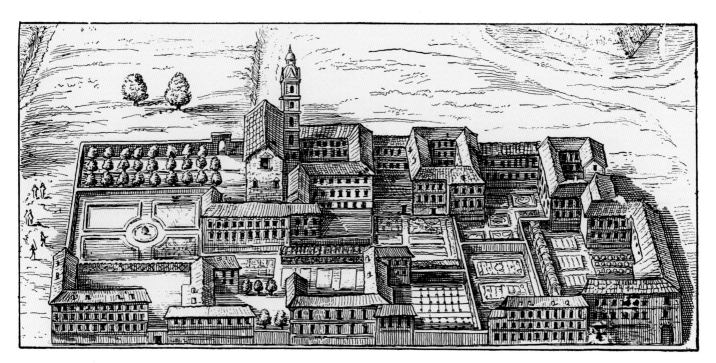

planting out; in the summer, weeding, trimming and harvesting; and in the autumn the final cutting back, digging and preparation for winter.

Once the herbs were harvested, they were taken to the herbarium, also the province of the herberer, where they were hung up in bunches to dry. Herbs such as fennel or poppy were suspended with their seed heads in linen bags, so that after a good shaking, the seeds could drop into the bag and be saved. Some of the seeds were set aside for culinary or medicinal use, others were stored for sowing the following spring.

The herberer had a wide knowledge of the properties of his plants. He made the various ointments, liniments and medicines that the infirmarer, in charge of the hospital, required. These preparations included garlic, horehound, thyme and angelica and elecampane for coughs and colds; sage and mallow for sore throats; fennel and mint for digestive problems; lemon balm, camomile and borage to soothe and relax; marjoram and parsley for rheumatism; rue, cornflower and clary sage for sore eyes; clover and yarrow for wounds and sores; and the opium poppy to dull severe pain. This last, because of its powerful effect and the danger of addiction if it fell into the wrong hands, may have been grown in a locked area of the garden, together with the other potentially hazardous plants, such as foxglove

used for heart problems and deadly nightshade used as a sedative.

In the kitchen, parsley, hyssop, savory, thyme, lovage, chives and garlic improved the flavour of the thick bean or pea soup, known as pottage, which was the staple diet in most monasteries. Mint, parsley, fennel and marjoram went into sauces for fish, and the abbot's roast lamb needed thyme. Ale was flavoured with alecost and bog myrtle, and bread with coriander seeds.

Southernwood, wormwood and pennyroyal were the favourite insect repellents. Mullein stems were dipped in tallow to make candles. The stems formed a kind of wick which burned with the wax. Rosemary was burned in a dish with other herbs or precious ingredients, such as frankincense, and used as an incense.

Somewhere in the herb garden may have been a plot dedicated to the Virgin Mary, for many plants were associated with her. It could have contained woodruff, cowslips, violets, lily of the valley, thyme and pennyroyal, and would have been an area of especially quiet reflection.

A view of a Turin monastery in 1682 showing the herb gardens on the right.

Sage was used for cleaning teeth and also as a cure for sore throats. In the abbot's kitchen, it was used to make rich meats more digestible.

HOME-MADE PORK *and* HERB SAUSAGES

Home-made sausages are fairly quick to make and children will love helping to shape them. Serve the sausages with mashed potato and gravy or bay leaf and oregano sauce (page 122). Chill any leftover sausages and eat them cold.

SERVES 4 (MAKES 8 SAUSAGES)

2tbsp oil
1 large onion, finely chopped
1 fat garlic clove, crushed
400g • 13oz good-quality, lean minced pork, lamb or beef
75g • 2½oz breadcrumbs
1 egg yolk
2tbsp finely chopped fresh parsley

2tbsp finely chopped fresh thyme
2tbsp finely chopped fresh marjoram
Salt and freshly ground black pepper
Oil

Heat the oil in a pan and gently fry the onion for about 10 minutes, until softened. Stir in the garlic and fry for 1 minute. Remove the pan from the heat and allow the onions to cool. Combine the remaining ingredients (except the oil) in a bowl and stir in the onions. Mix well. Divide the mixture into eight and shape each portion into a sausage shape, about 10cm/4in long. Chill in the refrigerator for 30–60 minutes.

These sausages are delicious baked, grilled or fried. To bake them, preheat the oven to 180°C/375°F/gas mark 4, put the sausages in a greased ovenproof dish and bake for 35–40 minutes. To grill them, preheat the grill to high, line a grill pan with foil and brush the foil with oil. Grill the sausages for 10–12 minutes, turning them occasionally, until cooked through. To fry the sausages, heat 1–2 tablespoons of oil in a large frying-pan over a medium heat and gently fry the sausages for 10–12 minutes, turning them once during cooking. If you are making a gravy to serve with the sausages, make it in the same frying-pan and scrape up any bits of meat left in the pan to enrich it.

BAKED CHICKEN *with* CHIVES *and* TARRAGON

This dish is perfect both for a family supper and for a dinner party. Leave the chicken to marinate overnight and then pop it straight into the oven. If you are running short of time, you don't even need to thicken the sauce: simply serve it straight from the oven. Serve with buttered noodles, rice or potatoes and a green vegetable.

SERVES 4

4 skinless, boneless chicken breasts
5cm • 2in piece of fresh root ginger, peeled and grated
1tbsp clear honey
1tbsp soy sauce

4tbsp dry white wine
2tbsp finely chopped fresh chives
2tbsp finely chopped fresh tarragon
1tsp cornflour

Make several deep incisions across the surface of each chicken breast. Put the remaining ingredients (except the cornflour) in a small bowl and mix well. Place the chicken breasts in an ovenproof dish large enough to hold them in one layer and pour over the sauce. Cover the dish with foil and leave to marinate in the refrigerator for at least 2 hours or overnight, turning once.

Preheat the oven to 190°C/375°F/gas mark 5. Turn the chicken breasts once more and replace the foil cover. Bake in the oven for 30 minutes, until the chicken is cooked. Transfer the chicken to a warmed serving dish and pour the cooking liquid into a small saucepan over a high heat. Mix the cornflour with 1 tablespoon of cold water and add to the pan. Bring the sauce to the boil and cook for 2–3 minutes, until it has thickened slightly. Serve each chicken breast with a little of the sauce.

CHICKEN *and* VEGETABLES *in a* POT *with* BOUQUET GARNI

If possible, this dish should be made in a very large casserole dish that can be used on the hob. A bouquet garni of parsley stalks, bay leaf and thyme gives a subtle herb flavour to the gravy made from the cooking juices.

SERVES 4

3tbsp oil
125g • 4oz thick piece of smoked bacon, cut in 1cm • ½in cubes
2 carrots, peeled and cut in 2.5cm • 1in chunks
2 celery stalks, cut in 2.5cm • 1in pieces
12 button onions, peeled but left whole
2 leeks, trimmed and cut in 2.5cm • 1in pieces
1 garlic clove, crushed
1.5 to 1.75kg • 3 to 4lb whole chicken (without giblets), rinsed and patted dry

300ml • ½ pint chicken stock
250ml • 8fl oz dry white wine
Salt and freshly ground black pepper
3 or 4 fresh parsley stalks, 1 fresh bay leaf and 3 fresh thyme sprigs, tied into a bouquet garni
125g • 4oz flat-cap mushrooms, quartered
1tbsp cornflour, mixed with 1tbsp cold water
3 to 4tbsp single cream (optional)

Preheat the oven to 180°C/375°F/gas mark 4. Heat 1 tablespoon of the oil over a high heat in a large casserole, add the bacon and fry until golden, stirring occasionally. Using a slotted spoon, transfer it to a dish and set aside. Add the remaining 2 tablespoons of oil to the pan with the carrots, celery, onions, leeks and garlic and fry until browned. Remove the vegetables and add them to the reserved bacon. Add the whole chicken to the pot and brown it on all sides. Then return the vegetables and bacon to the pan, pour over the stock and wine, season and add the bouquet garni. Bring to a simmer, then cover the chicken with foil and bake in the oven for 1 hour, occasionally basting the chicken with the cooking juices.

Stir in the mushrooms and cook for a further 30 minutes. Leave the foil off for the last 15 minutes, to allow the breast to become crisp. Test if the chicken is cooked by inserting a skewer into the thigh; the chicken is cooked once the juices run clear. Transfer the cooked chicken to a warmed serving dish and cover with a dome of foil, to keep warm. Remove the vegetables and keep warm. Discard the bouquet garni and put the casserole over a high heat. Bring the cooking juices to the boil, add the cornflour and stir until thickened. Check the seasoning, stir in the cream, if using, and pour into a warmed gravy jug.

To serve, arrange the vegetables around the chicken and serve the gravy separately.

USING HERBS AS FLAVOURINGS

The following recipes are fairly quick and easy ones. Often, you may have bought a whole packet of herbs when you only need just 1 or 2 tablespoons and therefore need to use some up, or you may have a glut of homegrown herbs. The recipes are, of course, good enough to justify buying herbs just to make them!

FLAVOURED OILS

Flavoured oils used to be made by gently crushing herbs and adding them to oil, which was then left for several weeks, if not months, before being used. However, the thinking nowadays is that you should heat herbs in the oil, so their flavour infuses into the oil, and then discard them, to prevent any bacteria present on the herbs from multiplying in the airless environment of the oil. Make small batches of flavoured oils, keep them in the fridge and use them within 1 to 2 days.

MAKES 6TBSP

6tbsp extra-virgin olive oil   *3tbsp fresh herbs, gently crushed*

Gently heat the oil in a small pan and add the crushed herbs. Cook gently for 5–10 minutes, to allow the flavour of the herbs to infuse into the oil. Allow the oil to cool, then strain into a suitable container, such as a glass bottle. Use the flavoured oil as you would olive oil, such as for tossing pasta, for salad dressings, in mayonnaise and for frying.

FLAVOURED VINEGARS

To really enjoy the flavour of a herb vinegar, prepare it a couple of weeks in advance to make sure the flavour is sufficiently developed. Add a fresh sprig or two of the chosen herb at the final bottling stage, for ease of identification and for decoration. Herb vinegars make delightful presents and, with a little help from an adult, children can make them as gifts for relations. Use the flavoured vinegar in salad dressings and sauces. Particularly popular herb vinegars are dill and tarragon but you can use almost any herb.

MAKES 1 LITRE · 1¾ PINTS

45g · 1½oz fresh herbs
1 litre · 1¾ pints white or red wine vinegar

Fresh herb sprigs, to garnish

Put the herbs in a glass container with a tightly fitting lid (or several containers) and pour over the vinegar. Cover and store in a dark place at room temperature for 1–2 weeks, gently shaking the bottle once a day. After this time, strain the liquid through a muslin-lined sieve into pretty glass bottles and add a fresh sprig or two of the herb used for flavouring. The vinegar will keep for several months in a cool, dark place. In sunlight, the sprig of herb will quickly lose its colour.

HERB BUTTERS

Herb butters can be used in a multitude of ways, such as over hot pasta, on top of steaks, for making garlic bread and for serving with bread. Almost any herb can be used but basil, tarragon, chives, parsley and coriander are particularly delicious. Try combinations of herbs, such as parsley and chives, and chervil and tarragon.

MAKES 125G · 4OZ

125g · 4oz butter, at room temperature

3tbsp finely chopped fresh herbs

Soften (but do not melt) the butter, by beating it in a bowl with a wooden spoon. Stir in the herbs, mixing well. Lay a piece of cling film on the work surface and spoon the butter on to the film in an oblong shape. Carefully wrap the butter in the film and roll it to form a fat tube, about 15cm/6in long. Place the butter in the refrigerator to harden. As and when required, unwrap it and cut it in slices.

Alternatively, spoon the butter into small ramekins, chill in the refrigerator and serve from the ramekins at the table.

87

LOIN OF PORK *with* FRESH SAGE *and* ONION STUFFING

Sage is synonymous with stuffings and makes a particularly good accompaniment to pork. Here, sage and onion stuffing is used to fill a boneless loin of pork, which is then roasted with strips of bacon.

SERVES 4 TO 6

1 boneless loin of pork tenderloin, weighing 1 to 1.25kg • 2 to 2½lb	STUFFING
	1tbsp oil
Salt and freshly ground black pepper	1 large onion, finely chopped
5 streaky bacon rashers, de-rinded	4tbsp white breadcrumbs, made from day-old bread
1tbsp plain flour	3tbsp finely chopped fresh sage
300ml • ½ pint dry cider	1 egg, beaten

Preheat the oven to 180°C/375°F/gas mark 4. To make the stuffing, heat the oil in a frying-pan and gently fry the onion for about 10 minutes, or until softened. Allow the onion to cool slightly, transfer to a bowl and mix in all the other stuffing ingredients.

Slice horizontally through the loin of pork, stopping about 2.5cm/1in from the second edge, so that the meat can be opened out like a book. Open the meat, season it with salt and pepper and spread the stuffing over one half. Replace the other half, arrange the rashers of bacon along the top of the meat and tie the meat into a neat shape with kitchen string at 2.5cm/1in intervals.

Place the meat in a roasting tin and roast in the oven for 60–70 minutes. Transfer to a carving board and cover with a foil dome, to allow the meat to rest while you make the gravy. Spoon off all but a tablespoon of the fat from the roasting tin and then put the tin over a medium heat on top of the hob. Stir in the flour and mix with the bits left in the bottom of the pan. Gradually pour in the cider, stirring well to prevent lumps forming. Increase the heat and boil the gravy to thicken it slightly. Once it has thickened, transfer to a warmed gravy boat.

Carve the pork into thick slices and serve with the gravy.

PORK CHOPS *in a* CIDER, SWEET MARJORAM *and* CREAM SAUCE *with* APPLE AND POTATO MASH

Pork chops cooked in cider and cream is a traditional dish that is enhanced by the addition of sweet marjoram.

SERVES 4

4 pork escalopes	MASH
15g • ½oz butter	425g • 14oz green eating apples, peeled, cored and quartered
3 shallots, finely chopped	
300ml • ½ pint dry cider	425g • 14oz potatoes, peeled and cut in chunks
5tbsp single cream	
3tbsp finely chopped fresh sweet marjoram	30g • 1oz butter
	3tbsp milk
	Salt and freshly ground black pepper

First, put the apples and potatoes in a large saucepan and cover with water. Bring to the boil and simmer for about 20 minutes. Then drain, return them to the pan and set aside with the lid on. Put the pork escalopes between two sheets of greaseproof paper and strike them gently with a meat mallet to flatten them to about 1cm/½in. Melt the butter in a frying-pan, add the shallots and fry gently for 5 minutes, until softened. Add the escalopes and fry them on both sides for about 3 minutes. Remove to a warmed plate and keep warm.

Pour in the cider, increase the heat and boil rapidly until it has reduced by a quarter. Stir in the cream, seasoning and marjoram. Return the escalopes to the pan and heat them for 1 or 2 minutes. Meanwhile, put the pan with the potatoes and apples over a medium heat and shake it to evaporate off any moisture. Mash the apple and potatoes with the butter and milk. Season well. Once the escalopes are heated through, serve with the mash.

89

The Chelsea Physic Garden

Founded in 1673 by the Society of Apothecaries, the Chelsea Physic Garden in London has undergone periods of expansion and decline. It is now one of the best known medicinal herb gardens in the world, and provides a green haven in the busy city as well as a centre for research into the healing properties of plants.

James I, who granted the charter to the Society of Apothecaries in 1617.

The Chelsea Physic Garden was a place where apothecaries could study medicinal plants.

A plan of the Chelsea Physic Garden, dated 1751 (far right).

When the Society of Apothecaries received their charter from James I in 1617, they immediately set up a training programme for their apprentices. This included not only the treatment of disease, but the recognition and cultivation of the many healing plants that were in the apothecary's pharmacopoeia, or handbook of medicines. Students were taken on local field trips and on "simpling voyages" (collecting medicinal plants) to places as far away as Wales and the Isle of Wight. Wherever they went, they collected specimens which were brought back to London and planted in the gardens of their colleagues and masters. The plants survived, but viewing them in their widely scattered plots was a time-consuming business. The Apothecaries needed one large garden that could be shared by them all.

In 1673, they persuaded Charles Cheyne, owner of the Manor of Chelsea, to rent them a plot of land with a frontage on the River Thames for £5 a year. All the plants were brought to this one spot. The garden became well established, and in 1683 the Apothecaries began a scheme of exchanging seeds and plants with Leeds University. By the beginning of the 18th century, however, enthusiasm for the garden had waned and it was looking slightly neglected.

In 1712, the Manor of Chelsea was bought by Dr (later Sir) Hans Sloane. He had studied at the garden during his medical training and had developed an interest in it. He granted the Apothecaries a lease at the original rent provided they maintained the garden properly.

A new head gardener was appointed, glasshouses were built for the plants that were being discovered abroad, and for a time all went well. By the 19th century, however, herbal medicine was in decline; there were no apothecaries, and nobody wanted the garden. From 1887, under the protection of the Trustees of London Parochial Charities, it was used by botany students at the Royal College of Sciences in nearby South Kensington.

The Physic Garden survived but did not flourish until 1981, when it was handed over to a new body of trustees. An appeal was launched with the aim not only of restoring the garden to its original beauty, but also to re-establish it as a centre for research and education. By 1987, sufficient funds had been raised, and in 1993 the garden was opened to the public for the first time.

The Chelsea Physic Garden is now better cared for and more informative than it has ever been. Its principal feature is the "medicinal walk". This begins at the informal beds containing the herbs that were there in Sir Hans Sloane's day, together with some dye plants and unusual vegetables. Then come the glasshouses where visitors walk through a tropical rainforest atmosphere, home to plants such as pepper, ginger and turmeric, and herbs used by Australian Aborigines and by Zulu warriors. Outside once more, you pass the perfumery and aromatherapy border and a bed of poisonous plants. There is a plot that illustrates the history of herbal medicine, and another portraying systems of herbal healing the world over. Elsewhere there are walks shaded by ancient trees and beds depicting plant families and the history of the garden itself.

The garden is once again an important place for herbal research. Bodies such as the English Gardening School, the botany department of the Natural History Museum and the Glaxo pharmaceutical company carry out projects there and contribute to the garden's income. With the growing interest in herbal cures, the Chelsea Physic Garden seems set to thrive.

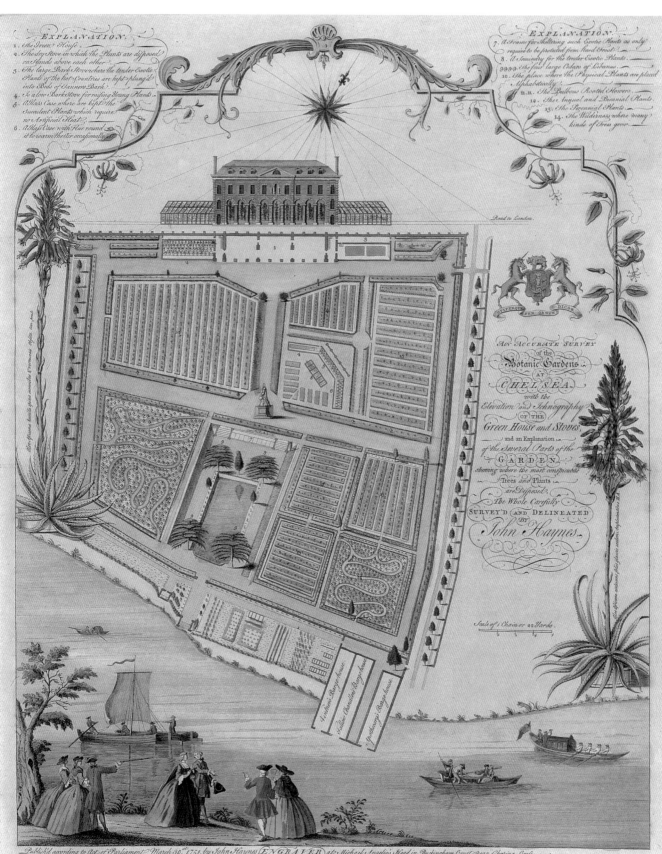

CHAPTER FOUR

FISH AND SHELLFISH

*C*arefully chosen herbs complement the subtle flavours of fish and shellfish, and their colour also brightens the appearance of many fish dishes. From traditional parsley to exotic Thai basil, herbs enhance sauces, marinades, and savoury butters for all kinds of fish.

FISH AND SHELLFISH

Herbs taste good with white fish, smoked fish, oily fish and shellfish. Parsley is the classic fish herb. Use it to liven up a Victorian-style kedgeree made with smoked haddock and rice. Mix it with chives and breadcrumbs to create a crispy topping for cod, or with lemon zest crumbs to form a coating for plaice. Stirred with chives and capers into mayonnaise, it is an ideal fish accompaniment.

Chives beaten into unsalted butter also make a rich addition to skate wings baked in lemon juice. Pungent fresh coriander, together with ginger and spring onions, gives an Eastern flavour to halibut steaks;

and Thai basil leaves, chillies, lime juice and coconut milk combine to produce a spicy dish of prawns.

Herbs that first grew on the shores of the Mediterranean are all good with fish. Sprigs of thyme and rosemary, tied with bay leaves and placed inside trout before grilling, impart a subtle flavour. Make a marinade for monkfish with thyme, oregano, oil and lemon juice; serve red mullet in a red wine sauce flavoured with thyme and fennel seeds; or toss oregano into a dish of pasta and seafood. Sorrel, with its fresh, acidic leaves, goes superbly well with oily fish, particularly salmon.

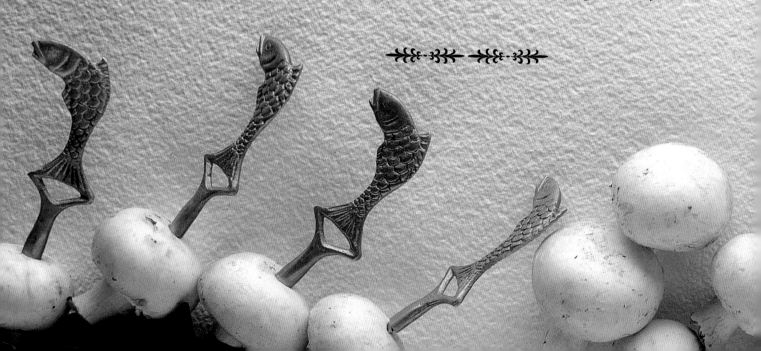

Marchande et Vendeur de Poissons, *W. van Mieris, 1713.*

95

COD *with* MIXED HERB CRUST

Choose plump, square fillets from the middle of the fish for this dish, rather than fillets from the tail end. To upgrade this to dinner-party status, simply add the herb and caper mayonnaise on page 108. Serve accompanied by new potatoes and a green salad or vegetables.

SERVES 4

60g • 2oz breadcrumbs, made
  from fresh brown bread
4 x 180g • 6oz cod fillets
4tsp black-olive tapenade
3tbsp finely chopped fresh
  parsley

3tbsp snipped fresh chives
4tbsp finely chopped fresh dill
30g • 1oz butter, cubed
Salt and freshly ground black
  pepper

Preheat the oven to 200°C/400°F/gas mark 6. Spread the breadcrumbs out on a baking sheet and toast them in the oven for about 5 minutes, making sure they do not burn. Spread the top of each cod fillet with a teaspoon of tapenade and set aside while you make the herb crust. Combine the breadcrumbs with the herbs and season well. Place a quarter of the mixture on top of each cod fillet, pressing down quite firmly. Transfer the fillets to a greased ovenproof dish and dot each one with pieces of butter. Bake in the oven for 15 minutes, until the fillets are tender and the crust is golden brown.

SALMON *with* SORREL SAUCE

Sorrel has a slightly sharp, lemony flavour and combines very well with fish. Salmon with sorrel sauce is a classic French recipe and makes a sophisticated dinner-party dish, accompanied by new potatoes and green vegetables.

SERVES 4

4 medium-size salmon fillets	SAUCE
125g • 4oz sorrel, stalks removed and leaves shredded	60g • 2oz butter
	4 shallots, finely chopped
	1 garlic clove, finely chopped
90g • 3oz young spinach leaves, stalks removed and leaves shredded	450ml • ¾ pint dry white wine
	3 fresh parsley stalks
	3 fresh tarragon sprigs
150ml • ¼ pint single cream	1 fresh thyme sprig
1tsp Dijon mustard	
Salt and freshly ground black pepper	

First make the sauce. Melt 30g/1oz of the butter in a saucepan and gently sauté the shallots for 4 minutes, until softened. Add the garlic and sauté for a further minute. Pour in the wine and add the parsley stalks, tarragon and thyme.

Bring to the boil and then leave to simmer until the sauce is syrupy and has reduced by about half.

Remove the pan from the heat and strain the liquid into a jug, squeezing the shallots and herbs to extract all the juice. There should be about 150ml/¼ pint of liquid: if there is less, make it up with vegetable stock; if there is more, use all of it. Discard the shallots and herbs left in the sieve.

In a separate pan, melt the remaining butter, add the sorrel and spinach leaves and cook gently for about 3 minutes, until the leaves have wilted. Add the white-wine syrup to the pan, stir in the cream and mustard and check the seasoning. Bring to the boil and simmer for a couple of minutes. Place the sauce in a food processor and purée until fairly smooth. Return the sauce to a clean saucepan and heat through very gently.

Meanwhile, preheat the grill to high and line a baking sheet or the grill pan with foil. Season the salmon fillets with black pepper and grill for 5 minutes. Then move the fillets closer to the grill and grill for a further 2 to 3 minutes, until the top is crisp and golden.

Once the sauce has heated through, arrange the fillets on four warmed plates and surround each with some of the sauce. Serve immediately.

SKATE *with* BUTTERY CHIVE SAUCE

This is a very light dish. Chives, with their mild onion flavour, go particularly well with fish and here they are mixed with a butter that is simply melted slowly over the fish after it has been grilled. Serve with a salad or boiled potatoes and vegetables.

SERVES 4

4 skate wings, weighing about 275–300g • 9–10oz each	BUTTER
½ a lemon	*60g • 2oz unsalted butter, softened*
Salt and freshly ground black pepper	*4tbsp snipped fresh chives*

To make the butter, add the chives and seasoning to the butter and beat with a wooden spoon until mixed well. Wrap the butter in cling film and put it in the fridge to harden.

Preheat the grill to high. Line a baking sheet with foil and lightly brush it with oil. Arrange the skate wings on the tray, skin-side up, squeeze over a little lemon juice and grill for 4 minutes. Turn the fish over, squeeze over a little more lemon juice, season with black pepper and grill for a further 3–4 minutes. Transfer the skate to warmed plates, add a slice of the chive butter and allow to melt slightly before serving.

PRAWNS *with* SWEET THAI BASIL

Thai basil leaves are available in Oriental supermarkets; if you cannot find them, substitute Mediterranean basil leaves which are more common. Coriander can also be bought from Oriental supermarkets with the roots intact; alternatively, use a tablespoon of chopped coriander stalks. Once you have made the highly aromatic paste, this dish takes just 10 minutes to cook. Serve with boiled rice.

SERVES 4

3 coriander roots	*150ml • ¼ pint vegetable or fish stock*
1 garlic clove	
1 red chilli, deseeded and sliced	*1tsp sugar*
5 black peppercorns	*1tsp salt*
1tbsp peanut or vegetable oil	*20 Thai sweet green basil leaves*
125g • 4oz Thai long beans or fine green beans, cut in 2.5cm • 1in pieces	*20 raw tiger prawns, defrosted if frozen, shelled*
1tbsp light soy sauce	*250g • 8oz oyster mushrooms, torn into bite-size pieces*
2 kaffir lime leaves or 1tbsp lime juice	
400g • 13oz can of coconut milk	

Grind the coriander roots, garlic, chilli and peppercorns in a pestle and mortar to form a paste. Heat the oil in a frying-pan or wok over a high heat, add the paste and fry for 1 minute. Add all the other ingredients, except the prawns and mushrooms, bring to the boil and cover. Reduce the heat and simmer for 5 minutes. Stir in the prawns and mushrooms and simmer for 3 minutes, until the prawns are cooked and have turned pink. Serve immediately.

John Josselyn, 17th century

John Josselyn arrived in New England, USA, in 1663, with the sole purpose to "discover all along the Natural, Physical, and Chirurgicall [Surgical] Rarities of the New-found World." Until then, little work had been done to discover and record the medicinal plants of America. Early European settlers had taken their own plants and seeds with them, but everyone knew there must be a wealth of useful native flora to be explored.
John Josselyn not only studied the plants, but he consulted and observed the American Indian herbal

practitioners. The result was New England's Rarities Discovered, *published in 1672.*
The book demonstrated how people's immediate natural surroundings could supply many of their medical needs, and therefore became highly popular in settlers' households. Many of the remedies found their way into the American pharmacopoeia.
Unfortunately, after John Josselyn, there was little exchange of information between the settlers and the native inhabitants.

Herbs from Ancient Egypt

The ancient Egyptians were one of the first peoples to study herbs for culinary, medicinal and aromatic uses. Herbs and spices were placed in tombs to see the soul through the afterlife and on altars as offerings to the gods. For the great and the lowly, herbs were an essential part of everyday life, and in rural Egypt today people follow the same tradition.

No Egyptian herbal has survived the centuries intact, but fragments written in hieroglyphs have come down from the 2nd century AD. From these and from tomb evidence we know that there were favourite herbs and spices. Coriander was offered to the gods in temple ceremonies, and used in poultices for treating broken bones. Fenugreek was grown as a salad vegetable, and employed medicinally to induce childbirth and increase lactation. The seeds of black cumin (similar to the modern love-in-a-mist) were sprinkled on bread, and prescribed to treat itching skin.

A modern herb and spice market in Cairo, Eygpt.

Basil

Basil is sowen in gardens in earthen pots . . . it is good for the hart and for the head. The seede cureth the infirmities of the hart, taketh away sorrowfulnesse which cometh of melancholies, and maketh a man merrie and glad.

GERVASE MARKHAM, 1631

Cumin itself was a remedy for colic and digestive disorders. Garlic, eaten daily, was a general tonic and a cure for chest ailments; and juniper was used for embalming.

Three hundred and twenty kilometres (200 miles) into Egypt's western desert is the Kharga Oasis and near the ancient market town of Kharga, in Baqat Wells, is the recently developed Medicinal Plant Garden. Despite the fact that rainfall is almost non-existent, this garden holds a wide variety of plants that are important to present-day Egyptian herbal medicine. There are guava trees, unknown to the pharaohs, but today providing fruit to treat upset stomachs. The flowers of hibiscus plants make a traditional tisane called *karkade*, which is sweetened with sugar, and acts as a restorative after long journeys. The seeds of

hibiscus are reputed to be an aphrodisiac. They are chewed to sweeten the breath and calm the nerves. Basil was known as the "royal herb" by the ancient Egyptians, and the variety grown in Baqat Wells is the spectacular aniseed basil, which can rise to 1 m (3 ft) high with a profusion of pale pink flowers.

In the town of Kharga itself, there is a herb and spice market, where local women buy herbal remedies for family illnesses, cosmetic herbs (such as henna to give their hair colour and sheen), and herbs and spices for cooking. Fresh herbs are sold in bunches. The dried herbs and the spices fill bulging sacks and woven rush baskets, or are piled loosely in pyramid shapes, creating an exotic display that suffuses the air with a tantalising aroma and transports you to the land of the pharaohs.

Eygptian female herbalists squeezing an animal skin filled with herbs. This method was used to extract the juice from herbs for use in medicinal cures.

Trout Stuffed *with* Mediterranean Herbs

Trout is no longer as expensive as it once was and is available all year round, making this dish ideal for a family supper. Ask your fishmonger to butterfly the fish, leaving the head and tail intact. No single herb is dominant in this recipe, which uses a combination of fresh Mediterranean herbs. Serve with new potatoes and vegetables.

SERVES 4

2tbsp olive oil
1 garlic clove, crushed
2tbsp finely chopped fresh flat-leaved parsley
4 medium-size trout, butterflied, with head and tail on
4 fresh thyme sprigs
4 fresh oregano stalks
4 bay leaves
4 fresh rosemary sprigs

Combine the olive oil, garlic and parsley in a small bowl. Make three or four slashes on both sides of each fish and rub the flavoured oil over the surface of each fish and into each incision. Meanwhile, divide the remaining herbs into four bunches (as for bouquet garnis), each bunch containing one of each herb, and tie with cotton or thin string. Put one bunch in the cavity of each fish and leave for 1 hour.

Preheat the grill to medium-high. Line a baking sheet with foil and brush it with oil. Arrange the fish on the sheet and grill for 4 minutes on each side. Serve immediately, reminding your guests about the bunch of herbs in the cavity of each fish.

These fish are also delicious barbecued. Simply put each fish inside a wire fish griller or wrap each fish in oiled foil and place directly on the barbecue grill.

Monkfish Kebabs *in a* Thyme *and* Oregano Marinade

Herbs are a common ingredient in many marinades as their flavour is easily infused into the other marinade ingredients. Thyme and oregano both have a strong Mediterranean feel to them, so pop these kebabs on the barbecue and think of balmy summer days by the sea. Serve with salad or boiled rice and vegetables.

SERVES 4

750g • 1½lb skinless, boneless monkfish tails
12 large, fresh bay leaves
16 to 24 button mushrooms

Marinade
5tbsp olive oil
2 garlic cloves, crushed
2tbsp finely chopped thyme leaves
2tbsp finely chopped oregano leaves
2tbsp lemon juice
Salt and freshly ground black pepper

If you are using wooden skewers (you need 8–12), soak them in cold water for 1 hour, to prevent them from burning.

Remove any remaining membrane from the monkfish using the point of a sharp knife. Cut the monkfish tails into 2.5cm/1in cubes and put them in a shallow dish. Combine all the marinade ingredients, pour them over the fish and mix well, to ensure that all the fish is coated in the marinade. Cover and leave for 1 hour, in the refrigerator.

Preheat the grill or barbecue to high. To make the kebabs, thread a cube or two of monkfish alternately with a button mushroom on to each skewer, wrapping a bay leaf around one cube of monkfish on each kebab. Brush the grill pan with oil and grill the kebabs for 4 minutes on each side, or until cooked through. Baste with any leftover marinade during cooking.

RED MULLET *with* RED WINE *and* THYME SAUCE

For this dish, red mullet fillets are required. Ask the fishmonger to fillet the fish and give you the head and bones for the sauce. Fresh, sweet-smelling thyme is ideal for the rich, red wine sauce. A potato gratin or sauté potatoes with vegetables is the ideal accompaniment.

SERVES 4

3tbsp olive oil
4 medium-large red mullet, filleted, head and bones reserved
3 garlic cloves, quartered
1 leek, sliced
2 shallots, roughly chopped
1 carrot, sliced
1 bay leaf
Small bunch of fresh thyme
2tbsp fennel seeds
600ml • 1 pint full-bodied red wine
150ml • ¼ pint vegetable stock
Salt and freshly ground black pepper

Heat 2 tablespoons of the oil in a saucepan and gently fry the fish head and bones for 3–4 minutes. Stir in the garlic, leek, shallots, carrot, bay leaf, thyme and fennel seeds and cook for a further 5 minutes. Pour in the red wine and stock, season well and bring to the boil. Reduce the heat and simmer, covered, for 25 minutes.

Remove the lid and simmer for a further 5 minutes, to reduce the sauce. Strain the sauce into a small pan, cover, and keep at a very low simmer while you pan-fry the fish.

Heat the remaining tablespoon of oil in a frying-pan and gently fry the red mullet fillets for 3–4 minutes on each side. Transfer the fish to warmed serving plates and serve immediately, accompanied by the sauce.

104

Samuel Hahnemann, 1755–1843

Samuel Christian Friedrich Hahnemann.

Samuel Hahnemann was the founder of homeopathy. He was a German physician, qualified in conventional medicine, who was also an experimental chemist. He was disillusioned with the bleeding, blistering and mercury treatments of orthodox medical practice and certain that he could find a more effective alternative. During experiments with the plant cinchona, used as a cure for malaria, he found that if it was taken by a healthy person it produced malaria-like symptoms. These symptoms, he discovered, stimulated the body's natural immune system.

With a few pupils, he began experimenting with other plant cures and soon determined that the smaller the dose, the more effective it was. This became the basis for homeopathy. Samuel Hahnemann developed 95 remedies, mostly plant-based, but some of mineral or animal extraction.

Regular doctors despised his work but, by 1813, homeopathy had become very popular in Germany and was beginning to spread to other parts of Europe.

Hans B. Gram, an American medical student of Danish descent, heard about homeopathy on a trip home to Copenhagen. In 1825 he opened America's first homeopathic practice, in New York City.

Steamed Halibut *with* Coriander

Steaming is a very healthy way of cooking fish as there is no added fat and the fish retains most of its vitamins and minerals. Coriander is an intensely fragrant herb and, as the fish steams, it picks up the herb's aroma. Coriander is found in many cuisines including Thai, Chinese, Indian, Turkish, Portuguese and North African. Serve accompanied by boiled rice and stir-fried vegetables.

SERVES 4

4 halibut fillets or steaks
60g • 2oz bunch of fresh
  coriander
4 spring onions, thickly sliced
2.5cm • 1in piece of fresh root
  ginger, peeled and thinly
  sliced

To garnish
Fresh coriander sprigs
2 spring onions, sliced
  diagonally

To serve
2tbsp soy sauce (optional)

Make two or three slashes across both sides of each halibut fillet or steak. Line the base of a steamer with half the coriander and a few of the slices of spring onion and ginger. Put the fish on top and cover with more spring onions, ginger and the remaining coriander. (If there is not room in the steamer to put the fish in a single layer, use a double-tiered steamer or steam them in two batches, keeping the cooked fish warm.) Cover the steamer and put it over a pan of simmering water. Steam the fish for 10 minutes, until it is tender. As a rough guide, cook the fish for 10 minutes for each 2.5cm/1in of its thickness. Measure the fish at its thickest part and calculate the cooking time from this.

Remove and discard the coriander, spring onions and ginger and transfer the halibut to a warmed serving dish. Garnish with sprigs of coriander and slices of spring onion and put the soy sauce in a small bowl for dipping the fish into, if you wish. Serve immediately.

The Herb Garden, Cloisters Museum, New York

Hop on a bus in New York's Madison Avenue, travel for about an hour past Columbia University and Washington Heights and through Spanish Harlem and, on the very northern tip of Manhattan, you reach a hilltop outside beautiful Fort Tryon Park. Within a few minutes you can be transported into medieval Europe.

The Cloisters Museum, donated by John D. Rockefeller Jnr, belongs to the Metropolitan Museum of Art in New York. Although it was constructed in the 20th century, it incorporates parts of five original medieval cloisters and is distinctly medieval in appearance. It was built to serve as an appropriate backdrop for medieval works of art which may have seemed out of place in a modern building in central New York.

Best known of the Cloisters Museum exhibits are the beautiful unicorn tapestries which were woven in Brussels at the beginning of the 16th century and which show seven scenes telling the story of the hunt of the unicorn. The backgrounds of all the principal pictures of these tapestries are scattered with embroidered flowers, some known and others fanciful. The museum, surrounded by herb gardens, is an apt setting.

Outside, the grounds are divided into three main cloister gardens: the Trie, the Cuxa Cloister Garth and the Bonnefont. They are all places of interest and tranquillity, and all quite different. Go straight from the unicorn tapestries to the Trie cloister garden and you will find the images come to life, for this garden contains all the recognised plants from the tapestries. The Cuxa Cloister Garth garden, inside an enclosed courtyard, is bordered with beds of medieval and modern herbs. Around the central fountain are well-kept lawns crossed by a pattern of paths. In winter, the open walkways are covered over by glass, providing an ideal environment for pots of aloe, bay, citrus trees, acanthus, jasmine and rosemary.

Step inside the Bonnefont cloister garden and you return to the peace of a medieval monastery. Although the design is not based on any particular monastery garden, it has all the typical features of such a place. It is enclosed by a wattle fence, and there are raised beds and a central well surrounded by four quince trees. It contains 250 species of plants that are known to have been grown in monastery gardens throughout the entire medieval period. It is a place for enjoyment and for quiet reflection.

After exploring the gardens you can sit on the terrace, surrounded by pots of fragrant trees, and enjoy the views of Fort Tryon Park, the Hudson River, George Washington Bridge and the State of New Jersey.

To leave off the properties of Simples, we come now to the conveniences of a Garden, which are manifold in respect of Speculation, by which I mean mere walking, or at most, but gathering such things as please them, which I count no labour, for that I intend to oppose as the practicall use. That there is no place more pleasant, may appear from God himselfe, who after he made Man, planted the Garden of Eden.

WILLIAM COLES, *ART OF SIMPLING*, 1657

A courtyard herb garden at the Cloisters Museum. The garden contains a variety of both medieval and modern herbs (far right).

Crumbed Plaice *with* Herb *and* Caper Mayonnaise

A combination of herbs and capers is known as *salsa verde* or *sauce verte*, meaning "green sauce" in Italian and French respectively. Here, the sauce has been added to mayonnaise and makes a great accompaniment to the plaice.

SERVES 4

150ml • 5fl oz milk
90g • 3oz very fine white breadcrumbs, made from 1–2 day-old bread
1tsp grated lemon zest
2tbsp finely chopped fresh parsley
4 plaice fillets, skinned and cut in half
3–4tbsp vegetable oil

MAYONNAISE
3tbsp finely chopped fresh flat-leaved parsley
1tbsp snipped fresh chives
2tbsp capers, finely chopped
1tsp wholegrain mustard
1tbsp lemon juice
6tbsp mayonnaise
Pinch of salt and white pepper

First make the mayonnaise. Combine all the ingredients in a small bowl and mix well. It should resemble a coarse paste. If it is too lumpy, blend in a food processor or pestle and mortar for a few seconds, to break down any lumps. Set aside, to allow the flavours to develop, while you prepare the fish.

Season the milk with salt and pepper and mix the breadcrumbs with the lemon zest, parsley and seasoning. Dip each piece of fish in the milk and then into the breadcrumbs, coating each piece well.

Heat half the oil in a large frying-pan and shallow fry half the fillets for 2 minutes on each side, until golden. Drain them on kitchen paper, then fry the remaining fillets. Serve immediately, with the herb and caper mayonnaise.

KEDGEREE

In Victorian days, kedgeree was to be found as one of many dishes laid out on a groaning sideboard at breakfast time. Nowadays, it is more likely to be eaten at brunch, lunch or as a late supper. Although kedgeree is a meal in itself, it can be accompanied by a salad or some vegetables, if you prefer. The parsley stirred through during the final stages of cooking really livens up the dish.

SERVES 4

500g • 1lb smoked haddock fillets	*2tsp hot curry powder*
5 black peppercorns	*200g • 7fl oz long-grain white rice*
1 bay leaf	*Juice of half a lemon*
3 eggs	*3tbsp chopped parsley*
90g • 3oz butter	*Salt and freshly ground black pepper*
1 onion, finely chopped	

Put the eggs in a pan of cold water, bring to the boil and then leave to simmer for 10 minutes. Drain the eggs and refresh them under cold water.

Meanwhile, poach the smoked haddock fillets in 600ml/1 pint of lukewarm water in a medium-size saucepan. Place over a medium heat and bring gently to the boil, then reduce the heat and leave to simmer for 5 minutes. Remove the haddock fillets and keep them warm.

Strain the poaching liquid into a jug. Put the rice in a sieve and rinse it thoroughly under cold running water.

Next, melt half the butter and gently sauté the onion with the curry powder for 10 minutes, until softened. Stir in the rice and mix well, to ensure the rice is coated with the onions and spices. Make up the poaching liquid, using water, to 400ml/13fl oz. Pour it over the rice and stir briefly. Bring to the boil and then reduce the heat. Cover with a tightly fitting lid and leave to simmer for 15–20 minutes, until the rice is tender and the liquid has been absorbed. (If the liquid is absorbed too quickly, add additional water.)

Meanwhile, remove the skin from the fish and flake the flesh into large chunks. Peel the eggs and chop them. Once the rice is tender, stir in the fish, eggs, lemon juice, chopped parsley and seasoning. Stir carefully, then cover and cook over a very gentle heat for a further 5 minutes.

Stir in the remaining butter and serve immediately.

SEAFOOD PASTA *with* OREGANO

White fish fillets, prawns and squid combine with tomato and oregano to make a delicious pasta sauce. This dish should be served as soon as possible after cooking, otherwise the squid and prawns may become tough and chewy.

SERVES 4

300g • 10oz tagliatelle	*300g • 10oz plaice fillet, skinned and cut into 2.5cm • 1in cubes*
2tbsp olive oil	
1 onion, chopped	
2 garlic cloves, crushed	*125g • 4oz tiger prawns, shelled and defrosted if frozen*
1tsp chilli flakes	
625g • 1¼lb canned chopped tomatoes	
	2 small squid tubes, cut into rings (optional)
3tbsp finely chopped fresh oregano	*90g • 3oz wrinkled black olives*
Salt and freshly ground black pepper	*Fresh oregano leaves, to garnish*
300g • 10oz cod fillet, skinned and cut into 2.5cm • 1in cubes	

Cook the tagliatelle in a large pan of boiling water for 10–12 minutes, or until cooked. Drain and transfer the pasta to a warmed serving dish to keep warm.

Meanwhile, heat the oil in a frying-pan and add the onions. Fry gently for about 10 minutes, until softened but not browned. Add the garlic and chilli flakes and fry for a further minute. Stir in the tomatoes, oregano and seasoning, bring to the boil and then leave to simmer, uncovered, for about 15 minutes. Add the cod and plaice and leave to simmer for a further 2 minutes. Stir in the prawns, squid rings and olives, and simmer for a final 2 minutes.

Check the seasoning and put a couple of spoonfuls of the sauce into the pasta and toss well. Pour the remaining sauce over the pasta, garnish with oregano leaves and serve immediately, accompanied by a mixed salad and bread.

CHAPTER FIVE

SAUCES, RELISHES AND DIPS

erbs add savour to all the best dishes. Spice up a meal with a herb-flavoured sauce; accompany a main dish with a tasty relish; make a herb-flavoured dip for crispy vegetable sticks; or toss a fresh green salad in a herb dressing.

Sauces, Relishes and Dips

Herb-flavoured sauces, relishes, dressings and dips all help to make meals exciting and appetising. Sauces can be based on a variety of ingredients. Tomato sauces can take on many guises, depending on the herbs and other flavourings used. With bay leaves and oregano, tomatoes make a sauce for pasta; and with coriander and chillies, they become a Mexican salsa. The combination of tomatoes, coriander, coconut, chillies, sugar and vinegar, simmered together until syrupy, gives a relish with a distinctly Oriental flavour.

Red peppers can be roasted and puréed to make a sauce base that is particularly delicious when flavoured with rosemary.

The combination of pine nuts, olive oil, Parmesan cheese and basil produces pesto, a classic pasta accompaniment.

Crème fraîche makes a creamy sauce base. Flavour it with dill and you have a wonderful companion for fish.

Dill and yogurt combine to make a simple cheese, known in the Middle East as labna; *and a mixture of garden herbs with cream cheese provides a quick and easy dip.*

A classic French dressing or a well-made mayonnaise will always turn a selection of raw vegetables into a delectable salad. Flavour it with a blend of fresh herbs that complements the other constituents of the meal.

113

Flowers and herbs in a distillery garden, German manuscript, 1521.

COCONUT *and* CORIANDER RELISH

Sweet relishes make ideal accompaniments to spicy foods and cold platters. Ready-grated fresh coconut is occasionally found in Oriental supermarkets. If none is available, crack open a coconut, peel off the brown skin and grate the white flesh yourself.

MAKES ABOUT 500G • 1LB

180g • 6oz ready-grated fresh
   coconut (or grate the flesh of
   1 coconut, weighing
   300–375g • 10–12oz)
180g • 6oz granulated sugar
120ml • 4fl oz white vinegar

¼tsp cayenne pepper
½tsp salt
500g • 1lb tomatoes, peeled, de-
   seeded and roughly chopped
4tbsp roughly chopped fresh
   coriander leaves

Put the coconut, sugar, vinegar, cayenne pepper and salt in a saucepan with 400ml/14fl oz of water and cook over a low to medium heat, covered, for about 30 minutes. Add the tomatoes and simmer, covered, for a further 30 minutes until the mixture becomes syrupy. If the mixture is not yet syrupy, uncover, and simmer for a further 10 minutes. Remove the relish from the heat and allow it to cool. Stir in the coriander.

If you are making this to keep, once the relish has cooled, transfer it to sterilised jars and seal. Store in the refrigerator. Use within a month of making.

ROASTED RED PEPPER *and* ROSEMARY SAUCE

This sweet sauce is a good accompaniment to fish, meat, poultry and vegetables. You can make it in advance and then reheat it. If you do this, do not remove the sprigs of rosemary until the sauce is reheated, to allow a deep rosemary flavour to develop.

MAKES ABOUT 300ML · ½ PINT

4 large red peppers
4tbsp olive oil
4 fresh rosemary sprigs
250–300ml · 8–10fl oz
  vegetable stock

1tsp lemon juice
Salt and freshly ground black
  pepper

Preheat the oven to 180°C/375°F/gas mark 4. Halve each pepper and remove the white pith and seeds. Put the pepper halves on a foil-lined baking sheet or in an oven-proof dish, pour over the oil and add a few broken sprigs of rosemary. Roast the peppers in the oven for 30 minutes.

Once the peppers have roasted, push them into the middle of the baking sheet or dish and cover them with a glass bowl. Leave to cool for about 10 minutes, then peel. Put the peppers in a food processor, along with any cooking juices or oil, and purée until smooth. Transfer the purée to a saucepan, add the remaining rosemary, the lemon juice and sufficient vegetable stock to make a pouring consistency and simmer gently for about 10 minutes. Check the seasoning. The sauce is now ready to serve.

CREAMY DILL SAUCE *for* FISH

This sauce is particularly suitable for fish dishes and is very quick and easy to make.

MAKES ABOUT 200ML · 7FL OZ

1tbsp olive oil
2 small shallots or 1 small
  onion, finely chopped
200ml · 7fl oz crème fraîche

1tsp lemon juice
2tbsp chopped fresh dill
Salt and freshly ground black
  pepper

Heat the oil in a small saucepan over a medium heat and gently sauté the shallots or onion for about 5 minutes, until softened. Stir in the crème fraîche and lemon juice and allow the crème fraîche to melt. Simmer for 1 minute, then stir in the dill. Season and serve immediately.

Maud Grieve, 1858–1929

Mrs Grieve, as she was known by the time of her death, was born in Islington, London, and when she was first married, travelled extensively in India.

On their return, she and her husband settled at a house called "The Whins," at Chalfont St Peter in Buckinghamshire, and set about growing a wide range of herbs. By 1914, "The Whins" was known as "Whin's Vegetable Drug Plant Farm and Medical Herb Nursery," and Mrs Grieve had acquired a great knowledge of her subject.

At the beginning of the First World War, the British government advocated the growing of medicinal herbs to replace those that had previously been imported. A lot of people with small plots of land became enthusiastic growers, and Mrs Grieve began writing pamphlets and running courses at "The Whins" on all aspects of cultivating and using herbs. She did a good deal to revive the herb industry in England, only for it to suffer a slump after the war when cheap imports returned.

Mrs Grieve had intended to collect all her pamphlets into a book, but she died before this could be done. Her vast store of information was collated by Mrs C.F. Leyel and finally published in 1931. Although slightly outdated, it is one of the most comprehensive books on herbs ever written, containing details of the botanical, medicinal, culinary, historical and mythical aspects of herbs. It continues to be widely read by herb lovers.

115

CORIANDER SALSA

Salsa is a traditional tomato sauce frequently eaten with Mexican food; it's hot and spicy, just like the type of Latin-American big-band dance music that shares its name. Many different recipes can be found for making salsa, with some using just raw ingredients and others cooked. This is a cooked salsa that has been tried and tested over several years. Serve as an accompaniment to tortilla chips, fried meats and poultry and all Mexican dishes.

MAKES ABOUT 250G • 8OZ

230g • 7½oz canned chopped tomatoes
3 small shallots or 1 small onion, roughly chopped
1 fresh red chilli, de-seeded and finely chopped
4tbsp roughly chopped fresh coriander leaves

Put all the ingredients in a food processor and process for about 10 seconds, so that the salsa still has a little texture. Transfer to a small saucepan and bring to the boil. Reduce the heat and simmer for 5 minutes, then allow to cool.

FRESH BASIL PESTO

Fresh pesto is delicious served with a piping-hot bowl of pasta. Making pesto the traditional way in a pestle and mortar gently squeezes and tears the basil leaves, imparting a delicious, full flavour. It should keep for up to a month in the refrigerator; simply store it in a jar, covered with a thin layer of oil.

SERVES 4

1tbsp pine nuts
45g • 1½oz Parmesan cheese, roughly crumbled
1 fat garlic clove, quartered
5tbsp extra-virgin olive oil
25 fresh basil leaves, roughly torn

TO GARNISH
Freshly grated Parmesan cheese
Salt and freshly ground black pepper

Fresh pesto can be made slowly, with a pestle and mortar in the traditional way, or quickly, using a food processor in the modern way. If a pestle and mortar are available, use these to purée all the ingredients gradually together; it takes about 25–30 minutes to form a delicious, aromatic paste.

Alternatively, put all the ingredients in a food processor and blend for a couple of seconds. The texture can vary from quite rough to very smooth, depending on your choice.

To serve, put a spoonful of pesto on the middle of each guest's dish of hot pasta and invite them to toss the sauce through the pasta. Offer additional freshly grated Parmesan cheese and salt and black pepper.

Herbs for Bees and Butterflies

One of the most pleasurable experiences of the summer is to sit on a warm, sunny day and watch the bees and butterflies hovering over a garden of fragrant herbs.

A herb garden can provide all that bees and butterflies need. The bees come for pollen to make honey, while the butterflies are seeking food, a place to lay their eggs and, eventually, somewhere to hibernate.

In the times when bee skeps (hives made from straw) were used, bee-keepers rubbed the inside of new skeps with herbs such as mint, lemon balm, sweet cicely or wild thyme in the belief that a swarm would be attracted to the sweet scents. They also made sure that the same fragrant plants grew in profusion nearby.

The natural oils of the plants from which the bees gather the pollen affect the flavour of the honey, so plants were chosen to give the preferred flavour. Wild thyme seems to have been the favourite. The poet Spenser called it "bee-

An arch of honeysuckle above a bed of herbs will always attract bees and butterflies to the garden.

Bees love fragrant herb flowers. Plants such as lemon balm growing near a hive encourage them to stay.

A walled garden creates a still, warm atmosphere where bees and butterflies can collect pollen undisturbed.

> *What was Paradise, but a Garden and Orchard of trees and hearbes full of pleasure? and nothing there but delights?*
>
> WILLIAM LAWSON, 1617

Formal knot gardens were popular in Tudor times, especially with beekeepers. They provided pollen-rich flowers for the bees and were a delight to look at.

alluring thyme." Thomas Hyll, in his *Gardener's Labyrinth* of 1577, said: "The owners of hives have a perfite forsight and knowledge what the increase or yields of honey will be every year by the plentiful of small number of flowers growing and appearing on the thyme about the Summer solstice. For this increaseth and yeeldeth most friendly flowers for the bees, which render a colour and savour to the Honey."

Butterflies come into the garden from midsummer to early autumn. They feed in the sun on nectar-rich blue flowers and lay their eggs on suitable large leaves. They hibernate in the autumn, and herbs that have not been trimmed back could provide a suitable resting place.

PLANTING A BEE AND BUTTERFLY GARDEN

Neither bees nor butterflies like to be cold or to be buffeted by winds, so choose a sheltered, south-facing corner of the garden with a wall or fence behind it. A nearby shed or greenhouse will provide space for butterflies to hibernate, and a patch of nettles somewhere close will be an ideal place for them to lay their eggs.

Many of the herbs that are grown for culinary and aromatic purposes are loved by bees and butterflies. These include rosemary, lavender, bergamot (sometimes called bee balm), lemon balm (its Latin name *Melissa* was an old country name for a bee), basil, marjoram (particularly the variety known as golden marjoram), hyssop, savory, thyme, sage, woodruff, viper's bugloss and catmint (*Nepeta mussinii*).

Bees also love borage, clary sage, red clover, meadowsweet, poppy, nasturtium, mullein and wallflowers. "The Husbandman preserves it most in his Bee-garden," said Gervase Markham in the 16th century of the wallflower, "for it is wondrous sweet and affordeth much honey."

Butterflies love most of all the flowers of the buddleia bush, and this can be grown at the back of your bee and butterfly plot. They are also attracted to lilac, globe thistles, evening primroses, Michaelmas daisies, periwinkles and the ice plant (*Sedum spectabile*).

FRESH HERB MAYONNAISE

Making home-made mayonnaise is a very satisfying experience and the end result is absolutely delicious. To make a herb mayonnaise, simply stir in fresh herbs at the end. Practically any herb can be used, although the more "woody" ones, such as rosemary and thyme, are less suitable. The cheat's method of making herb mayonnaise is simply to stir a few tablespoons of chopped fresh herbs into commercially made mayonnaise and leave it to stand for 30 minutes to 1 hour, to allow the flavours to develop. Home-made mayonnaise will keep for up to a week in the refrigerator.

MAKES ABOUT 300ML · ½ PINT

2 large egg yolks *	*Pinch of ground white pepper*
1tsp Dijon mustard	*2tbsp finely chopped fresh herbs*
300ml · 10fl oz vegetable or	*(such as basil, tarragon,*
olive oil	*chives, chervil, parsley*
1tbsp lemon juice	*and/or coriander)*

Ensure all the ingredients are at room temperature. Put the egg yolks and mustard in a medium-size bowl and mix together. Next, with a hand-held electric mixer or food processor in motion, start to add the oil *very* slowly, starting with a single drop at a time and blending the mixture well before adding more oil. Always keep the mixer in motion and continue to add the oil drop by drop, until the mayonnaise starts to thicken. Once it starts to thicken, the oil can be added in larger drops but always make sure that you have incorporated all the oil before adding any more. Once you have added half the oil, add the rest in a steady stream. Continue blending until all the oil is used up and the mayonnaise is thick and creamy. Then stir in your choice of herbs, the lemon juice and pepper. For a deeper flavour, allow the mayonnaise to stand for 30 minutes to 1 hour, to let the flavours develop.

Do not be tempted to add the oil faster than a drop at a time at the beginning or the mixture will curdle and will not thicken. If the mayonnaise starts to curdle at any time, beat in 1 to 2 teaspoons of boiling water. If this fails, put another egg yolk in a clean bowl, very slowly add the curdled mixture one drop at a time and then continue as above.

*NOTE: Some eggs have been shown to contain salmonella so the elderly, young, babies, pregnant women and people with poor immune defence systems are advised not to eat raw or lightly cooked eggs.

FRESH HERB SALAD DRESSING

Liven up a bowl of salad leaves simply by adding a wonderful herb dressing. The dressing will keep for 4 to 5 days, but after that the herbs may start to deteriorate in flavour. Almost any herbs are suitable but, in particular, try basil dressing over a tomato and mozzarella salad, tarragon dressing over a chicken salad or dill dressing over a seafood salad.

SERVES 4

6tbsp extra-virgin olive oil	*1 to 2 tbsp finely chopped fresh*
2 tbsp white-wine vinegar	*herbs*
½tsp mustard powder	*Salt and freshly ground black*
	pepper

Combine all the ingredients in a screw-topped jar and shake well. Just before serving the salad, pour over half the dressing and toss well.

Store the remaining dressing in a cool, dark place, out of direct sunlight.

TWO MINT SAUCES

Mint is used in sauces all over the world; for example, in Britain mint sauce is ubiquitous with traditional roast lamb and in India *raita* is frequently served with spicy curries, to cool the palate.

TRADITIONAL MINT SAUCE FOR

ROAST LAMB	*2 to 3 tbsp chopped*
1tbsp granulated sugar	*fresh mint*
1tbsp boiling water	*3tbsp white-wine vinegar*

Dissolve the sugar in the boiling water in a small bowl. Add the remaining ingredients and leave for at least 1 hour before serving to let the flavours develop.

RAITA

½ small cucumber, peeled and	*2tbsp finely chopped*
grated	*fresh mint*
300ml · ½ pint natural yogurt	*Salt and white pepper*

Put the cucumber in a sieve, sprinkle it with salt and leave to drain for 15 minutes. Rinse the cucumber and squeeze out most of the juice. Put the yogurt in a bowl and stir in the cucumber, mint and seasoning. Allow to stand for 10–15 minutes to let the flavours develop.

BAY LEAF *and* OREGANO SAUCE *for* MEAT *and* PASTA

If you're looking for a variation on the usual tomato sauce for pasta and meat, try this one. It is quick to make, and can be made in advance and reheated. It is also suitable for freezing so, if there is a glut of tomatoes in the summer, make plenty of this sauce and freeze it.

MAKES ABOUT 600G • 1LB 3OZ

2tbsp olive oil
1 large onion, chopped
1 garlic clove, crushed
600g • 1lb 3oz fresh or canned tomatoes, chopped
8 bay leaves

1tbsp finely chopped fresh oregano
1tbsp tomato purée
Salt and freshly ground black pepper

Heat the oil in a large saucepan over a medium heat and gently fry the onion for 8–10 minutes, until softened but not browned. Stir in the garlic and fry for a further 2 minutes. Add the remaining ingredients and simmer, uncovered, for a further 15–20 minutes, stirring occasionally. The sauce is now ready to serve. It is an excellent accompaniment to the home-made sausages on page 84.

CREAM CHEESE *and* HERB DIP

Thinking up new ideas for dips that are quick and easy isn't always easy but here's one that can be made in just a couple of minutes. Change the herbs according to what is available in your garden or refrigerator, if you don't have the ones suggested here.

SERVES 2

200g • 7oz cream cheese
1tbsp chopped fresh chives
1tbsp chopped fresh flat-leaved or curly parsley
1tbsp chopped fresh tarragon
1½tbsp lime juice

Pinch of salt and white pepper

TO SERVE
Crudités, bread sticks, Melba toast or toasted pitta bread

Put the cream cheese in a bowl and beat until smooth. Add the remaining ingredients and beat again until well blended. If possible, leave the dip to stand for at least 1 hour, to allow the flavours to develop.

Samuel Thomson, 1769–1843

Samuel Thomson was the son of a farmer from Alstead in New Hampshire, USA. His circumstances were poor, he was born with a club foot and as a child he was always ill.

Conventional doctors, with their mercury-based medicines and techniques of bleeding and blistering, could do little for him, but he gradually improved under the care of the Widow Benton, a local herb-doctor who lived close to his parents.

By the time he was eight years old, Samuel Thomson had himself become extremely interested in the healing abilities of plants and, guided by the Widow Benton, he set about making his own discoveries, his most valuable being the healing properties of lobelia.

He stood by as conventional medicine failed to prevent the death of his mother, but when his daughter became ill and the physicians proclaimed her near to death, he took matters into his own hands. Dismissing the doctors, he instinctively held his sick child over a hot steam bath and watched as she began to relax and grow better. After her complete recovery, he made this treatment one of the basics of Thomsonian medicine.

Convinced that his methods were far more gentle and effective than those of the doctors, he used a system of fasting, steaming and about 65 herbal remedies first on his own family and later on his neighbours. He became famous throughout the country and successfully treated cases of yellow fever in New York in 1806.

GREEK YOGURT *and* DILL CHEESE

This type of cheese is known as *labna* in the Middle East where it is served as part of a meze, which is a selection of dishes served together as an hors d'oeuvre or light meal. Although the cheese has to be left to drain overnight, it is so simple to make it is well worth the wait. It can be served on its own as a starter or as one of a selection of dips and spreads.

Put all the ingredients into a bowl and mix well. Take a large piece of muslin, fold it in two and put it in a sieve. Pour the cheese mixture into the muslin, gather up the ends and tie them with string. Remove the bag from the sieve and hang over a bowl to drain overnight.

MAKES ABOUT 400G · 13OZ

400g · 13oz Greek yogurt
5tbsp finely chopped
   fresh dill
1 garlic clove, crushed
   (optional)

Pinch of salt and white pepper

TO SERVE
Bread sticks, toasted bread,
   pitta bread or crusty bread

123

CRANBERRY *and* SAGE SORBET

Cranberries are synonymous with Christmas and Thanksgiving. Here, they are joined by sage leaves to make a tangy sorbet. As sage has quite an overpowering flavour, just enough is added to reduce the sharpness of the cranberries. Many varieties of sage can be used, such as pineapple sage and icterina sage.

SERVES 4

250g · 8oz cranberries
125g · 4oz sugar
600ml · 1 pint water
150ml · ¼ pint orange juice, strained
30 sage leaves, roughly torn

Put the cranberries in a saucepan with half the water and bring to the boil. Once the skins have popped, stir in the sugar and simmer gently until it dissolves. Allow the mixture to cool slightly, then purée in a food processor and push through a sieve, to remove the skins and seeds. Stir in the orange juice.

Put the remaining water in a saucepan, with the sage leaves, and bring to the boil. Boil hard for about 5 minutes, until the liquid has reduced by just over half. Allow to cool, squeezing the leaves with a spoon occasionally to release all the flavour. Once the liquid has cooled, stir it into the cranberry purée and transfer to a plastic container. Cover the container with cling film and freeze until semi-frozen. Then remove, uncover and stir well or whisk with an electric whisk to break up the ice crystals. Return the sorbet, covered, to the freezer until it is frozen. Alternatively, follow the manufacturer's instructions for your ice cream/sorbet machine.

Remove the sorbet from the freezer 20–30 minutes before serving, to allow the sorbet to soften slightly. To serve, spoon the sorbet into stemmed glasses.

STRAWBERRY *and* ROSEMARY SORBET

This sorbet has a very subtle flavour of rosemary, which combines well with strawberry.

SERVES 4

125ml · 4fl oz water
125g · 4oz granulated sugar
2tbsp chopped fresh rosemary leaves (no stalks)
6tbsp lemon juice
500g · 1lb strawberries, hulled
175ml · 6fl oz good-quality, dry white wine, chilled

To Garnish
Strawberries, halved
Small fresh rosemary sprigs

Put the water, sugar, rosemary and 2 tablespoons of the lemon juice in a saucepan, bring to the boil and leave to simmer, until the sugar dissolves. Remove from the heat and allow the syrup to cool . Put the strawberries in a blender until smooth, then sieve them and add the remaining lemon juice. Strain the syrup through a sieve to remove the rosemary, stir into the strawberry purée and add the chilled wine. Mix well, transfer to a plastic container. Cover with cling film and freeze until semi-frozen, then uncover, remove and stir well. Return to the freezer, covered, until it is frozen.

Honey *and* Lavender Ice Cream

The fragrant, sweet scent of lavender comes from the stalks and leaves, not just the flowers. Lavender can be used to infuse cream and sugar syrups, to make great flavourings for ice creams, sorbets, cakes and soft drinks. Sweetened with honey, this ice cream tastes exactly as the flower smells.

SERVES 4

About 8–10 stalks and heads of fresh lavender
350ml • 12fl oz single cream
3tbsp clear runny honey (flavoured with lavender, if available)
45g • 1½oz caster sugar
3 egg yolks*
Lavender flowers, to decorate

Gently wash the lavender and pat dry in kitchen paper. Then place it in a saucepan, with the cream, and bring slowly to just below the boil. Remove from the heat and stir, in order to release the lavender's aroma. Leave the cream to cool completely, so that it is suffused with the full flavour of the lavender.

Once the cream has cooled, place the honey and sugar in a small saucepan with 6 tablespoons of water. Bring slowly to the boil, to dissolve the sugar, and then boil for 4 minutes, without stirring. Meanwhile, beat the egg yolks until thick and frothy. Once the sugar has boiled for 4 minutes, allow it to cool for 30 seconds and then pour it over the egg yolks in a steady stream, whisking constantly whilst pouring. Continue to whisk for about 5 minutes, until the mixture is thick. Strain the cream into the mixture, discarding the lavender, and continue whisking until the mixture is frothy and has cooled down.

Pour the mixture into a plastic container and place in the freezer. Once it is semi-frozen, remove from the freezer and whisk once again, to remove any ice crystals. Cover the container with foil or cling film and freeze until the ice cream is solid. Transfer the ice cream to the fridge 30 minutes before serving, to allow it to soften slightly, and serve decorated with lavender flowers.

*Note: It is essential to eat the ice cream within one week as it contains raw egg. Some eggs have been shown to contain salmonella so the elderly, young, babies, pregnant women and people with poor immune defence systems are advised not to eat raw or lightly cooked eggs.

Geranium *and* White Wine Sorbet

Infusing a sugar syrup with geranium (pelargonium) leaves imparts a subtle flavour of the smell of the leaf. Ensure that any leaves used have not been sprayed with pesticides or other chemicals. Use one of the more sweetly scented types of geranium, such as Mabel Grey, Corinda or Attar of Roses, rather than the spicier ones,

SERVES 4

15 sweet-scented geranium leaves
250ml • 8fl oz water
125g • 4oz granulated sugar
3tbsp lemon juice
250ml • 8fl oz chilled, good-quality, dry white wine
Geranium petals, to decorate

Wash the geranium leaves thoroughly and scrunch them in your hands to bruise them to release the flavour. Then place the water, sugar, geranium leaves in a large saucepan, bring slowly to the boil, to dissolve the sugar, and then simmer gently for 5 minutes. Remove the pan from the heat and allow the syrup to cool for a couple of hours.

Once the syrup has cooled completely, strain it through a sieve and discard the geranium leaves. Then stir in the lemon juice and the chilled wine. Mix well, transfer to a plastic container, cover with cling film and place in the freezer until half frozen. Remove, uncover and stir well to break up the ice crystals. Return the sorbet to the freezer, covered with cling film, until it is frozen. Alternatively, follow the maunfacturer's instructions for your ice cream/sorbet machine. To serve, spoon the sorbet into stemmed glasses and decorate with geranium petals.

General Index

Italics refer to illustration captions

A
air fresheners 22
Alcuin 6, 82
America 19, 22
American Indians 19, 24–5, 72–3
aphrodisiacs 11
apothecary *19*
Arabs 18, 22
aromatic herbs 22–5
Ashurbanipal, King 8
astrology 18
athlete's foot: remedy 21
Augustus Caesar *8*
Avicenna 18, 29

B
basil 27, *27*, 100, 101
bathing *22*, 29
bay 26, *26*
Beach, Wooster 19
beauty products 28–31
bees: herbs for 118–19
Beeton, Mrs Isabella 33
bergamot *9*
Bible 8, 22
blue flag 73
boneset 73
borage 26
bouquet garni 35
Bradley, R. 28
braised dishes 35–6
Breviary of Henry I of Este 77
bruises: remedy 21
burning perfumes 24–5
butterflies: herbs for 118–19
buttermilk and lime flower
    cleanser (recipe) 30

C
camomile *21*
candles 83; (recipe) 25
Carmelite Water 28–9
casseroles: using herbs in 35–6
Charlemagne 6, *6*, 82
cheese: herbs to use with 37
Chelsea Physic Garden 90, *90*, 91
chervil 26, *26*
Cheyne, Charles 90
Chinese 11, 18, *18*
chives 26, *26*
chopping herbs 34–5; equipment
    for 48
Christian legends 11
Cloisters Museum, New York:
    herb garden 106, *107*
Coles, William 106
comfrey *21*
common cold: remedy 21
companion planting 61
compresses 20, 21
coriander 26, *26*, 100

cosmetics 28, 30–1
costmary conserve (recipe) 35
Crusaders 8, 22
culinary herbs 32–3; methods of
    using 34–7
Culpeper, Nicholas 18, 19, 51
cumin 100–1
cuttings 14–15

D
dandelion 27, *27*
decoctions 20
demons: protection against 10
deodorisers 22
dill 26, *26*
Diocles of Carystius 18
Dioscorides 18, 44
dips 112
diseases: protection against 10
distillery garden *113*
division 15
dried herbs 7, 37
drying herbs 16–17, *16, 17, 65*

E
eggs: herbs to use with 37
Egyptians 8, 18, 22, 28, 29, 100–1
elderflower facial scrub (recipe) 28
essential oils 23
evil spirits: protection against 10

F
face mask (recipe) 29
facial scrub: elderflower (recipe) 28
Farmer, Fanny 33
fennel *10*, 26, *26*
fenugreek 100
fish: herbs to use with 37, 94
flea repellents 24
Floris, James *24*
France 11, 32, 33
freezing herbs 17

G
Galen 18, 71
garlic 26, *26*, 101
garnishes 36–7
Gerard, John 23
Glasse, Hannah 35, 37
gods and goddesses 10
Gram, Hans B. 104
gravel paths 13, *14*
Greeks 10, 11, 18, 22
green dumplings (recipe) 33
Grieve, Mrs Maud 115
growing herbs 12–15
guava 101

H
Hahnemann, Samuel 19, 104
hair rinse (recipe) 30
hair treatments 29

harvesting herbs 10, 16
henna 101
Henrietta Maria, Queen 28
herb gardens 7, 8–9, 12–13, *12, 13,
    15, 20*; monastic 82–3, *83*
herbal oil 20
herbal treatments in home 20–1
herbals 11, 18, 19, 31, *82*, 100
herbarium 83
herberer 82–3
herbs: directory 26–7; growing
    12–15; lore 10–11; preserving
    16–17; properties 6–7; uses 6
hibiscus 101
Hindus 10, 11
history of herb-growing 8–9
home remedies 20–1
homeopathy 19, 104
honeysuckle *118*
Hungary Water 28
Hyll, Thomas 119

I
immortal herbs 11
infusions 20, *20*, 21
initiation ceremony *72*
insect repellents 22, 83
Italy 10, 18, 33

J
James I 90, *90*
Josselyn, John 99
joutes 32, 33
juice extraction *101*
juniper 101

K
karkade 101
Kharga, Egypt 101
knot gardens 9, *9, 119*
Koran 22

L
Laplanders 11
lavender 26, *26*, 54–5; fields of *6,
    54*; lemon and lavender
        sweet bag mixture
        (recipe) 24
lavender bottles 54
lavender sugar (recipe) 55
lavender water (recipe) 55
lemon balm *12*, 26–7, *26, 118*
Leyel, Mrs C. F. 29, 31, 54, 115
lore of herbs 10–11
lovage *11*, 26, *26*
love charms 11

M
magical properties of herbs 10, 11
marjoram 27, *27*, 28
Markham, Gervase 100, 119
meats: herbs to use with 37, 76

medical herbalism 18–19
mints 27
monasteries 8, 18
monastery gardens 82–3, *83*
moth repellents 24
mouthwash 21
Myddfai: physicians of 79

N
nettle 27, *27*
nightmares: protection against 10
nutmeg *33*

O
oregano 27

P
parsley 10, *14*, 27, *27*
pasta dishes 36, 37
pâtés: using herbs in 36, 40
peppermint *21*
perfumes 22, 28
plantain *10*
planting herbs: lore 10
Platt, Sir Hugh 24
Pliny 28
pomanders 22
poppy: opium 83
pork: stuffing chine (recipe) 37
pot-pourri 22–3; (recipe) 23–4
pots: growing herbs in 14, *14*
pottages 32, 33, 83
poultices 20
poultry: herbs to use with 37, 76
preserving herbs 16–17
Price, Rebecca 35
propagation 14–15
protective herbs: lore 10
pulses: herbs to use with 37

Q
Queen Anne's Chafing Dish
    (recipe) 25

R
relishes 112
Rhode, Eleanor Sinclair 37, 9, 13
rice: using herbs with 36, 37
ritual cleansing 73
roasts: using herbs with 36
Rockefeller, John D. (Jnr) 106
rocket 26, *26*
Romans 8, 11, 18, 22, *22*, 29
root cuttings 15
root divisions 15
rose *22*
rose-water 29
rosemary 11, *11*, 27, *27*, *31*
Roxburgh Ballads *117*

S
sacred herbs 10
sage *21*, 27, *27*, 32, 83

sage brushes 25
salads 36, 37, 58
sauces 112
savory 27, *27*
scalp dance *72*
seed: collecting 83; growing herbs from 14
shaman *73*
shellfish: herbs to use with 94
Shen Nung 18
skin toner (recipe) 31; types 30
sleeplessness: remedy 21
Sloane, Dr Hans 90
smudge sticks 25
snacks 40
Society of Apothecaries 90
Society of Herbalists 31

sorrel 27, *27*
soups: using herbs in 35
sowing herbs: lore 10
Spain 11
spearmint 27, *27*
spices 33
Stacey, Susannah 55
starters 40
stews: using herbs in 35–6
still-rooms 22
stir-fried dishes 65
stomach, upset: remedy 21
storing dried herbs 17
stuffing: for chine of pork (recipe) 37; using herbs in 36
sweat lodges *73*

sweet bags 22, 24; lemon and lavender mixture (recipe) 24
sweet dishes 36, 37
"sweet herbs" 32, 33
symbolism of herbs 11

T

tarragon 26, *26*
Thomson, Samuel 19, 122
thyme *10*, *12*, 21, 27, *27*, *82*
tisanes 20, 21
toothache: mouthwash for 21

U

unguents 22, 28

V

van Mieris, W.: *Marchande et Vendeur de Poisson 95*
vegetables 36, 37, 58
Venus *28*
Virgin Mary 11, 83

W

walled garden *118*
weddings 11
window-boxes 14
wine cup (recipe) 35
witchcraft: protection against 10

Y

yarrow *21*

INDEX *of* RECIPES

A

apple and potato mash 89
arni psito 65
aubergines: baked aubergines with basil and oregano 53
avocado, wild mushroom and rocket salad with Italian dressing 67

B

basil: baked aubergines with basil and oregano 53
fresh basil pesto 117
pesto 65
prawns with sweet Thai basil 98
bay leaf and oregano sauce for meat and pasta 122
beans: minted bean and herb pâté with herbed bread sticks 53
winter beans with thyme, marjoram and parsley 68
beef: boiled beef with chive sauce 64
fillet of beef *en croûte* with herbs and red-wine sauce 78
borage: alcoholic summer punch 47
grape and cucumber cooler 46
bream: stuffed bream baked in red wine 64
broad beans with savoury sausage and mint 64
butter: herb butters 87

C

cabbage: shredded cabbage and spring greens with fennel and lemon balm 67
carrots: baby new carrots with crème fraîche and chervil 62
carrot and coriander purée 71

cheese: cream cheese and herb dip 122
pasta with rocket and dolcelatte 49
chervil: baby new carrots with crème fraîche and chervil 62
chicken: chicken with tarragon 64
country-style chicken pie 64
goujons of chicken with a soured cream and herb dip 43
Thai chicken curry with coriander and lemon grass 81
chives: boiled beef with chive sauce 64
skate with buttery chive sauce 98
chutney: coriander and mint chutney 65
coconut and coriander relish 114
cod with mixed herb crust 96
coriander: carrot and coriander purée 71
coconut and coriander relish 114
coriander and mint chutney 65
coriander salsa 116
prawn and coriander pâté 44
steamed halibut with coriander 105
Thai chicken curry with coriander and lemon grass 81
courgettes: herbed fried courgettes 61
cranberry and sage sorbet 124
cucumber: dill cucumbers 65
grape and cucumber cooler 46
raita 121
curry: sour fish curry 65
Thai chicken curry with coriander and lemon grass 81

D

dill: creamy dill sauce for fish 115
dill cucumbers 65
Greek and yogurt and dill cheese 123
pumpkin and dill soup 48
dips: cream cheese and herb dip 122
soured cream and herb dip 43
dressing: fresh herb salad dressing 121
Italian dressing 67
drinks: alcoholic summer punch 47
grape and cucumber cooler 46
herb tea 47
mint julep 46
non-alcoholic summer punch 46
duck breast with orange and mint 80

F

fennel: shredded cabbage and spring greens with fennel and lemon balm 67
fish: sour fish curry 65
frittata: summer savory and caramelised onion frittata with marinated olives 43

G

geranium and white wine sorbet 125
grape and cucumber cooler 46
gravad lax 64
Greek salad with oregano dressing 71
gulai tumis 65

H

habas a la Catalana 64
halibut: steamed halibut with coriander 105
honey and lavender ice cream 125

I

ice cream: honey and lavender ice cream 125

J

jugged venison 65

K

kebabs: monkfish kebabs in a thyme and oregano marinade 102
kedgeree 109
kidney beans: *lobio* 65

L

lamb: lamb with yogurt and mint sauce 80
roast lamb 65
lavender: honey and lavender ice cream 125
lemon balm: non-alcoholic summer punch 46
shredded cabbage and spring greens with fennel and lemon balm 67
lemon grass: Thai chicken curry with coriander and lemon grass 81
lettuce: peas with lettuce, parsley and chervil 50
lobio 65
lovage: potato and lovage soup 44

M

marjoram: pork chops in a cider, sweet marjoram and cream sauce with apple and potato mash 89
sweet marjoram pancakes 52
winter beans with thyme, marjoram and parsley 68

mayonnaise: fresh herb
mayonnaise 121
herb and caper mayonnaise 108
mint: alcoholic summer punch 47
broad beans with savoury
sausage and mint 64
coriander and mint chutney 65
duck breast with orange and
mint 80
lamb with yogurt and mint
sauce 80
mint julep 46
minted bean and herb pâté
with herbed bread sticks 53
non-alcoholic summer punch 46
raita 121
tabbouleh with parsley and
mint 63
traditional mint sauce for
lamb 121
monkfish kebabs in a thyme and
oregano marinade 102
mushrooms: avocado, wild
mushroom and rocket salad
with Italian dressing 67
herb and mushroom quiche 51
mushroom soup with parsley 45

O

olives: summer savory and
caramelised onion frittata
with marinated olives 43
omelettes: *tzvazegh* 65
onions: sage and onion stuffing 89
summer savory and caramelised
onion frittata with marinated
olives 43
oregano: baked aubergines with
basil and oregano 53
bay leaf and oregano sauce
for meat and pasta 122
monkfish kebabs in a thyme
and oregano marinade 102
oregano dressing 71
seafood pasta with oregano 109

P

pancakes: sweet marjoram
pancakes 52
parsley: mushroom soup with
parsley 45
peas with lettuce, parsley
and chervil 50
tabbouleh with parsley and
mint 63
winter beans with thyme,
marjoram and parsley 68
pasta: pasta with rocket and
dolcelatte 49
seafood pasta with oregano 109
pâté: minted bean and herb pâté
with herbed bread sticks 53
prawn and coriander pâté 44
peas with lettuce, parsley and
chervil 50
peppers: roasted red pepper and
rosemary sauce 115
pesto 65
fresh basil pesto 117
pies: country-style chicken pie 64
plaice: crumbled plaice with herb
and caper mayonnaise 108
pork: home-made pork and herb
sausages 84
loin of pork with fresh sage
and onion stuffing 89
pork chops in a cider, sweet
marjoram and cream sauce
with apple and potato mash 89
potatoes: apple and potato mash 89
potato and lovage soup 44
thyme-roasted potatoes 61
poulet à l'estragon 64
prawns: prawn and coriander
pâté 44
prawns with sweet Thai basil 98
pumpkin and dill soup 48

Q

quail: grilled quail stuffed with
tarragon 79
quiche: herb and mushroom
quiche 51

R

red mullet with red wine and
thyme sauce 104
relish: coconut and coriander
relish 114
Rindfleisch mit Schnittlauchsosse 64
rocket: avocado, wild mushroom
and rocket salad with Italian
dressing 67
pasta with rocket and
dolcelatte 49
rosemary: roasted red pepper and
rosemary sauce 115
strawberry and rosemary
sorbet 124

S

sage: cranberry and sage sorbet 124
sage and onion stuffing 64, 89
salad: Greek salad with oregano
dressing 71
herb salad 69
salmon: gravad lax 64
salmon with sorrel sauce 97
salsa mexicana 64
sauce: coriander salsa 116
creamy dill sauce for fish 115
raita 121
roasted red pepper and
rosemary sauce 115
salsa mexicana 64
traditional mint sauce for
lamb 121
sausages: broad beans with
savoury sausages and mint 64
home-made pork and herb
sausages 84
savory: summer savory and
caramelised onion frittata

with marinated olives 43
seafood pasta with oregano 109
skate with buttery chive sauce 98
sorbet: cranberry and sage
sorbet 124
geranium and white wine
sorbet 125
strawberry and rosemary
sorbet 124
sorrel: salmon with sorrel sauce 97
soup: mushroom soup with
parsley 45
potato and lovage soup 44
pumpkin and dill soup 48
spring greens: shredded cabbage
and spring greens with fennel
and lemon balm 67
strawberry and rosemary sorbet 124
stuffing: sage and onion stuffing 64

T

tabbouleh with parsley and mint 63
tarragon: chicken with tarragon 64
grilled quail stuffed with
tarragon 79
thyme: monkfish kebabs in a
thyme and oregano
marinade 102
red mullet with red wine and
thyme sauce 104
thyme-roasted potatoes 61
winter beans with thyme,
marjoram and parsley 68
trout stuffed with Mediterranean
herbs 102
tzvazegh 65

V

venison: jugged venison 65
vinegar: flavoured vinegars 87

Y

yogurt: Greek and yogurt and dill
cheese 123
raita 121

CREDITS

————

Key: *a* above, *b* below, *l* left, *r* right

Corbis-Bettmann 72*a*, 101, 107; Culpeper Ltd 31*bl* & *r*; ET Archive 9*b*, 11*a*, 19*a* & *b*, 32*b*, 36*al*, 59, 72*b*, 73*b*, 77, 82*br*, 90*a*, 91; Floris of London 24*a*; Food and Wine From France Ltd 33*br*, 37*a*; Garden Matters 37*b*, 118*br*; Herb Society, London 115; Hulton Getty 104; Image Bank 9*a*, 16, 20*a*, 36*b*, 100 (Infocus International); Mansell Collection 6*a*, 17, 25, 51; Clive Nichols 12*b*, 14*a*, 28*b*, 36*ar*, 64*a*, 82*a*, 106, 119; North Wind Picture Archives 8*a* & *b*, 13*b*, 18*a*, 22*a* & *b*, 23*l*, 28*a*, 32*a*, 33*ar*, 41, 73*a*, 82*bl*, 83*a*, 113, 118*al*; Pictor 7*a*, 54*al* & *br*, 55, 65*b*; Picture Bank Photo Library 6*b*, 10*bl* & *br*, 15*b*, 18*b*, 20*b*, 31*a*, 34*b*, 83*b*; Ann Ronan at Image Select 71; Harry Smith Horticultural Photographic Collection 7*b*, 11*b*, 12*a*, 14*b*, 15*a*, 29, 33*bl*, 64*bl*, & *br*, 118*ar*; Visual Arts Library 95; Elizabeth Whiting Associates 65*a*.
While every effort has been made to acknowledge copyright holders, Quarto would like to apologise if any omissions have been made.
All other photographs are the copyright of Quarto Publishing plc.

Author's acknowledgements (KH)
I would like to thank all those who helped during the writing and testing of the recipes in this book.
Thanks to Tim, Odette, Sue, Yvette and Steve, Richard and Claire, Simon and Lisa, Tony and Tina, Ken and Hazel, Melissa and Andy
and my family for all their support and ideas. Thanks also to my editor, Cathy Marriott, and the art editor, Clare Baggaley.